LEGENDS IN ACTION
Ten Plays of Ten Lands

LEGENDS IN ACTION

TEN PLAYS
OF
TEN LANDS

by
Nellie McCaslin

PLAYERS PRESS, Inc.
P.O. Box 1132
Studio City, CA 91614-0132

LEGENDS IN ACTION - Ten Plays of Ten Lands
© Copyright 2001, by Nellie McCaslin and Players Press, Inc.
ISBN 0-88734-633-2
Library of Congress Catalogue Number: 93-22161

Paste-up: Chris Cordero and Antony Pakkidis

PLAYERS PRESS, Inc., P.O. Box 1132, Studio City, CA 91614-0132

Simultaneously Published
U.S.A., U.K., Canada and Australia

Printed in Canada

Library of Congress Cataloging-in-Publication Data

McCaslin, Nellie.
    Legends in action : ten plays of ten lands / Nellie McCaslin ;
forward by William-Alan Landes
        p. cm.
    Includes bibliographical references and index.
    SUMMARY: A multicultural collection of short plays based on
legends from ten different countries.
    ISBN 0-88734-633-2
    1. Legends--Juvenile drama. 2. Children's plays, American. [1.
Folklore--Drama. 2. Plays.] I. Title
PS3563.C33745 L4 1999
812'.54--dc20
                                                            93-22161
                                                                CIP
                                                                 AC

FOREWORD

It is with great pleasure that I write these opening words for the publication of this collection of plays. I have known Nellie McCaslin far longer than she has known me; meeting her for the first time in the 1960's when I was acting in New York and my girlfriend was an undergraduate at New York University. Nellie was this fireball of children's theatre, she worked in all areas and was becoming a serious and important force for its future development.

As an educator, innovator and writer, Nellie was igniting the imaginations and driving a new force in the approaches to Children's Theatre. I had seen some of her workshops; I was working with Theatre Unique, off-off-Broadway and was intrigued with her approaches. I too wanted more fun in theatre with children. The old "sit still and be quiet" formula was torturing these new young audiences. Nellie was adding sparkle, fun and taking ideas from all aspects of life and incorporating them in theatre and theatre education. She was collaborating with the finest minds and leading them in a unified creative action. It was an exciting time, and it was New York, and it was theatre.

My own life and career pulled me away. I only periodically even heard about Nellie. My girl-friend, now a graduate student, would occasionally write a note on something she read or heard but it wasn't often or much and I was far too busy with my own life. I did notice, while acting and living in England, that Nellie had written the landmark *Creative Drama in the Classroom.* I did get to see a copy two years after it came out. Just from looking at it, I knew it was an important book.

By the 1970's I was in Los Angeles and working for the studios. I had started a publishing company in the mid-60's with a friend from Theatre Unique; mainly he thought my *Wondrawhopper* children's plays and musicals needed wider exposure than the current publisher was giving them. He also worked on our theatre magazine—*Showcase.* I did little in this area except add more *Wondrawhoppers,* after they were written and produced. I was building a film career in directing and producing, and dabbling in theatre to keep my juices flowing with Players U.S.A. But, Nellie kept crossing my desk and her works were always at hand.

Throughout the 1970's I heard and saw more of Nellie's works. I encountered students of Nellie's who were spreading her words. I saw her influence at numerous theatre gatherings. By the mid-80's I had left one movie studio and was headed to another. The publishing company, Players Press, had reached reasonable size for a small publisher and it needed help. While I was on hiatus, I attended several book conferences and we started publishing books as well as plays. There were so many books that needed to be published, so much that needed to be done, so many works that needed wider exposure... and, there was Nellie McCaslin.

I fell in love with a little lady. A fiery, red-headed-woman—Sharon Hoffman (Gorrell). I had known her earlier but she reappeared in my life in 1979 and by the mid-80's she too needed something. So I started educating her and building a bigger company, for her— she knew almost nothing about theatre, except the child like excitement it created in her, and it all just worked because she had the most lovable personality — a typical witch that captivated. I threw her into this world of children's theatre publishing and she came home with Nellie McCaslin. It was a surprise and a delight, maybe a touch of destiny. Nellie's books were dying, but Nellie said "I have never felt that the books were dying—only bruised and waiting for someone to come along and repair the damage. I was thrilled to have them picked up and republished by Players Press." A friend at Longman, one of Nellie's publishers, also came to us and said, would you like to help us sell her books? I couldn't understand their problem, Nellie's books, to me, were wonderful. She had expanded the *Creative Drama* concept and written two specialized texts, *Creative Drama in the Primary Grades* and *Creative Drama in the Intermediate Grades.* Her plays were out of print and several of her works had gone to University presses, which publish quality work but don't promote, so to me they were being forgotten. How could they be pushed aside, they were still fabulous! We needed to do something.

Sharon crawled into my arms one evening, at a convention, as I explained the fire I saw in Nellie's works and felt it was a waste to see this material disappear. In all her redheaded innocence she said the silliest thing, "Why don't you save it?" Ridiculous! But, by morning I had realized it was brilliant. Sharon spoke to Nellie and Nellie and I corresponded. I spoke to Longman; we were selling Nellie's books. I started to acquire the rights to her other works. Nellie sent us her plays. We signed contracts and today we publish most of Nellie's works and manage the licensing of all her plays, Nellie says she "...was delighted..." What I enjoy most is the little notes we get from time to time thanking us for her "wonderful little plays." and the notes from Nellie updating and clarifying for me.

Even today Nellie amazes me. She constantly writes articles, travels the world, teaches, acts and directs. I have asked her to rewrite again the *Creative Dramas.* We're republishing her plays in anthology and acting editions. We have updated her master work *Theatre for Children in the United States: A History* and a third edition of *Children and Drama...* best of all, I still get so many bright little letters and notes from Nellie telling me what she will be doing next and always asking when will I publish something for her.

I am delighted that, from such a distant acquaintance, Nellie became such an important force and friend in my life and work. I just hung up the telephone with Nellie telling me of her last two trips to Southeast Asia, her dinner theatre acting, and her writing. An amazing lady! I am as proud as I can be to see this latest edition come to fruition. I look forward to the future and more of Nellie McCaslin's adventures in the world of children's theatre. I know that Players Press and I will want to publish her adventures and share them with you.

William-Alan Landes

CONTENTS

INTRODUCTION

It is a great pleasure to have this collection of plays based on folklore made available at a time when cultural diversity is being stressed in our schools. The original considerations in the selection and dramatization of the material remains unchanged, however, for the tales have stood the test of time. The first consideration was to offer in dramatic form some of the most delightful folk tales of ten different countries. Although there are hundreds of myths and legends to be found in the literature of each, very few of them have been dramatized, in spite of the fact that they lend themselves as well to the stage as to storytelling and balladry.

It has been my aim to select, from this vast store, legends which are both ancient and beloved, as well as representative of the peoples from whom they came. The one exception is *Johnny Appleseed,* which is based on information we have concerning the life and activities of this legendary eccentric. The plot is original, however, and the facts and spirit have not been distorted for the sake of dramatization.

The second consideration was a matter of practicality. Many children's stories have not been adapted for the stage because of the technical problems they pose. I have tried to keep this collection as simple as possible in that respect so that the plays could be done in the classroom, with the focus on interpretation. There is no question as to the added effectiveness of an elaborate production, but the scripts themselves do not require it. Only three of them call for a scene change, and this can be accomplished easily if just the essential pieces of furniture or scenery are used. The other plays are written either in one act or one setting and are therefore simple to arrange.

The third consideration in dramatizing these tales was to provide the kind of material most suitable and most often sought for assembly programs. To meet this requirement I have avoided the long play, complicated plot, and small cast. The playing time of each runs from ten to fifteen minutes, not exceeding twenty in any instance. The dialogue is natural and appropriate for children in the intermediate grades. The use of a narrator dispenses with a printed program and helps explain more fully the background and setting of the action. As to the size of the casts, there is some variation, with an average of eight or more characters, and the option of adding others in large group scenes. In eight of the ten plays an entire class may take part. Strikingly different from the others is *Christmas Fiesta*. It is a festival rather than a play in that it depends upon costumes, dancing, song and audience participation for its effectiveness. After much consideration I decided to include it because of its origin in folklore and its importance as a tradition among the Mexican people. As a social studies project or as a program in which the objective is to become better acquainted with our neighbors to the south, *Christmas Fiesta* offers more in the way of custom and tradition than do any of the others. The breaking of the piñata at the end is fun for both players and audience, and can lead into a party for both. Production notes, floor plans, and costume suggestions follow each script; it is hoped that they will be helpful in planning and performing the plays.

Nellie McCaslin
New York City

LEGENDS IN ACTION
Ten Plays of Ten Lands

JOHNNY APPLESEED

An American Legend

THE legend of Johnny Appleseed is beloved as one of the few fragments of American folklore. In this dramatization, although the story is original, the background is legendary; and faithful re-creation of the spirit has been the aim. There is reflected the community's devotion to Johnny Appleseed, as well as their debt to him. They try to persuade him to settle down after a lifetime of wandering, but he makes them realize that his mission is one of "planting," not of "harvesting"; and so he goes on his way, in keeping with the legend. The homespun quality, the sturdy characters, and the spirit of neighborliness are all here, and they are essential, although the production itself may be one of the utmost simplicity.

CHARACTERS

JOHNNY APPLESEED, *about* 50, *kindly, rather ragged appearance*

MARK O'BRIEN, *a settler of middle age, husky, determined*

MRS. O'BRIEN, *his wife, a motherly woman, strong and courageous*

WILLIAM, *their elder son, aged* 16

EMILY, *their elder daughter, aged* 14

MARY, *their younger daughter, aged* 11

GEORGE, *their younger son, aged* 8

CY JAMES, *a new neighbor, young and eager to succeed*

ANNOUNCER

SCENE 1: *The O'Briens' cabin in Ohio; one autumn night.*

SCENE 2: *The same; the following morning.*
TIME: *Autumn of* 1840.

JOHNNY APPLESEED

SCENE ONE

THE SCENE is MARK O'BRIEN'S *cabin in Ohio during the middle of the nineteenth century. It is small and crude, furnished simply with the early settler's bare necessities. A table, three or four chairs, benches, and such things as bowls, kettles, woodpile, etc., will suggest the interior well enough.*

❖   ❖   ❖   ❖

ANNOUNCER. Some of the best-loved stories in America are those told about Johnny Appleseed. He was a young man who went out from New England to the wilds of nine Middle Western states to plant the first apple trees. Some people thought him crazy; few understood him, but all who knew him loved him. In our play, he is an old man, and on one of his last trips across Ohio. The scene is Mark O'Brien's cabin, and the characters are: Mark O'Brien, Mrs. O'Brien, their four children—William, Emily, Mary, and George—Cy James, a new neighbor; and Johnny Appleseed. As the curtain opens, it is twilight of an autumn day. The O'Brien family and their neighbor, Cy James, are sitting before the fireplace, talking, as the curtains open.

MARK. Well, Cy, are you glad you came down from Rhode Island to settle here?

CY. I sure am. This Ohio River Valley's the best country a man ever saw! When I get my land cleared, I'll have a farm that beats anything in New England.

MRS. O'BRIEN. When are you going to bring your wife out, Cy?

CY. Well, ma'am, as soon as I get my house built and my barn raised. She's staying with her folks in Providence, but she says she's all ready when I send for her.

MARY. Have you any little girls, Mr. James?

3

CY. No, Mary, not yet. But I hope we'll have a family like yours some day.

GEORGE. Well, when you do, we'll show 'em the path through the woods, and the best place to swim in the river, and when the boats come down, and——

MRS. O'BRIEN. Well, you children had better not do too much exploring of the woods—or the river either, for that matter. It's a wilderness here yet—with *all* our clearing; and unfriendly Indians still prowl the country.

EMILY. We just go as far as Mr. James's farm, Mamma; and there are always neighbors about.

MRS. O'BRIEN. All right—but no farther. (*To* CY.) How much land are you planning to clear, Cy?

CY. Oh, about thirty acres at first, ma'am. But if my crops grow, I'll clear more—plant orchards and gardens. It's flat and rolling as far as an eye can see.

MARK. Yes. No stones to break your spade and choke your young plants.

CY. (*Agreeing.*) No, sir. When I think of my father's place in New England!— Hills and rocks! Harder for him to keep things growing after forty years than for me to fell trees and make my first planting.

WILLIAM. Maybe Johnny Appleseed will come along and give you a hand with your orchard.

CY. Appleseed? Who's that?

MARK. You never heard of Johnny Appleseed? (CY *shakes his head.*) Why, he's a fellow came out here almost forty years ago from up Boston way. Came out to plant apple trees in all these Middle Western states—Pennsylvania, Ohio, Indiana. There isn't a farm around here that doesn't have some of his trees on it.

MRS. O'BRIEN. Funny thing about him is he never planted any for himself. Always for others. He started out a young man with a bag of seed on his back. And now all the orchards you see on your way out here grew from his first planting.

CY. And is that his real name—Appleseed?

MARK. (*Laughing.*) No—Jonathan Chapman. But he's been planting apples for so long that everybody calls him "Appleseed." Why, he's almost a legend in these parts.

CY. (*Musing.*) Johnny Appleseed. Is he likely to come by this winter?

MARK. Oh, you never can tell. As like as not. He comes sometimes in the spring, sometimes in the fall—and some years not at all. · He always stops here when he does come, though. Helped us raise our house and plant those first trees you see out there.

(*He points out the window, and* CY *goes to look.*)

MRS. O'BRIEN. Yes, and he planted my herb garden, too. Never was a man could make things grow like Johnny.

MARK. Always leaves a page of the Bible with a settler the first time he takes him in.

EMILY. He brings us toys, too.

MRS. O'BRIEN. Only when he comes from the cities. Most of the time he stops with farmers. He even spends a night with the Indians if there's no house around. They like him, too.

WILLIAM. Some folks think he's crazy. · Jake Cooper——

MARK. Never mind, Son. He's been the best friend we settlers ever had. And don't you forget it!

WILLIAM. (*Ashamed.*) No, sir.

GEORGE. (*Laughing.*) Remember the time the wasp got up his trouser leg?

CY. What happened then?

WILLIAM. Well, you see, he likes animals and insects as much as he does people. So when this hornet crawled up his leg and stung him, instead of killing it like anyone else would have done, he said, "Why don't you go home to your family? I've got a lot to do today!"

MARK. Same way with snakes! Walks right over them in his bare feet! Why they don't bite him, I'll never know. But none ever did.

MRS. O'BRIEN. He always said they were the Lord's creatures —just like the birds and bees. No, I doubt if Johnny'll meet his death in the wilderness. It'll be old age and hard work. No living thing could hurt him.

CY. (*Rising.*) Well, I suppose I better be going along down to my shack. It's getting dark out, and there aren't very good street lights around here.
(ALL *laugh at his little joke.*)

MRS. O'BRIEN. Why, Cy, the idea! After working for Mark all day, you think we'd let you go home to a cold supper? You just sit right down again while I put the plates on the table.

CY. (*Hesitating.*) I don't want to be any trouble to you, ma'am.

MRS. O'BRIEN. Trouble? No such thing! If there wasn't enough in this kettle for one more mouth, I'd be ashamed. It's just stew—New England boiled dinner and corn bread. But there's plenty.

CY. I'm much obliged, ma'am. I'd like to stay.
(*He sits again.*)

MRS. O'BRIEN. All right, then. Emily, you finish setting the table; and Mary, you go to the shed for the milk.
(*Both* GIRLS *obey.*)

MARK. Want to use my team next week, Cy?

CY. If I can help you out again, sir. I won't have my own mules for another month. And that's kind of late for the fall plowing.

MARK. Sure thing. You can come tomorrow and——

MARY. (*Rushing in from the shed with the milk.*) Mother! Father! There's a tramp coming through the woods! I saw him when I went for the milk!

MARK. (*Jumping up in alarm.*) You sure, child?

MARY. Oh, yes! He was all ragged! And he had some kind of bundle on his shoulder——

MRS. O'BRIEN. He wasn't an Indian?

MARY. Oh, no. He's walking along in the open. I couldn't see very well, but I know he——

MARK. Well, I think I'd better go take a look. (*Steps to the cabin door as* JOHNNY APPLESEED *approaches on the other side.*) Johnny Appleseed! Well, I'll be! We were just talking about you!

MARY. It's Mr. Appleseed, Mamma!

MARK. Where'd you come from, stranger?

JOHNNY. Pittsburgh, Mark. It's a long way.

MRS. O'BRIEN. For pity's sake! Ask him in, Mark! After all that trip, you let him stand talking in the doorway! How are you, Johnny?

(*She goes up to shake hands with him.*)

JOHNNY. Just fine, ma'am. It's good to see you all.

MARK. (*Introducing* CY.) And this is our new neighbor, Cy James, from down Rhode Island way. He's building next farm to us. Bringing his wife out in another year.

JOHNNY. (*Shaking* CY'S *hand warmly.*) Glad to know you, sir. Reckon I'll be seeing you again.

CY. I'm glad to know you, too. The O'Briens have been tellin' me all about you.

JOHNNY. (*As the children gather around him.*) And here's the rest of the family! Emily—and William! You've grown, son!

WILLIAM. Yes, sir. I'm sixteen now——

JOHNNY. And six feet, too, I'd say. Where's George?

GEORGE. Here I am, Mr. Appleseed! Did you bring us anything?

MRS. O'BRIEN. (*Scolding.*) George! For goodness' sake!

JOHNNY. That's all right, ma'am. He knows I wouldn't forget him. Right here in my knapsack. (*Pulls a book out of his knapsack.*) For William.

WILLIAM. (*As he takes it.*) Oh, thank you, sir! There aren't many of these out here, you know!

JOHNNY. And Emily . . .
(*Hands her a colored kerchief.*)

EMILY. Oh, Mr. Appleseed! Thank you! Isn't it pretty, Mamma?

MRS. O'BRIEN. (*Delighted, too.*) Yes, indeed, Emily.

JOHNNY. (*Drawing out the last two parcels—toys for the children.*) And Mary and George!

GEORGE. Oh, look!
(*He pulls a little wooden cart across the floor.*)

MARY. (*Holding up a little doll.*) And see mine!
(*The* CHILDREN *get down to play with their toys.*)

MRS. O'BRIEN. (*Apologetically.*) You must forgive them their bad manners, Johnny. They have so few toys— nothing but what Mark has time to make for them—that they forget to thank you properly.

JOHNNY. That's all right. I don't want any thanks. But I would like to stay overnight. And maybe Mark has an old pair of pants he's not using? (*Showing his ragged trousers.*) Those last few miles through Pennsylvania didn't do these any good.

MRS. O'BRIEN. Mercy, I should say not! Well, you just pull up a chair and have supper with us. And tonight I'll find something in the scrap box to make you some pants.

EMILY. (*Stepping away from the table that is now completely set.*) It's ready, everybody!

MARK. Well, come on, folks. You sit here, Johnny. And Cy, over there. You children in your regular places. (*All sit, and* MARK *lowers his head for grace.*) "Oh, God, bless our home, our family, friends, and neighbors, and give us thankful hearts for all thy mercies. Amen." (*All straighten up again.*) Now then, Johnny, how about some stew?

JOHNNY. Looks good to me! I haven't had a square meal in a couple of days.
(*Helps himself heartily.*)

MARK. And you, Cy, help yourself.

MRS. O'BRIEN. I'll get some more bread.
(*She rises and goes for it.*)

CY. Thanks, Mark. Nothing like work in the open air to give you an appetite.

JOHNNY. I remembered this stew—kept me going the last ten miles. Not as grand a cook between here and Pittsburgh as Mrs. O'Brien!

CY. Sure seems like home to me. I've lived off the fat of the land, thanks to these folks.

MARK. It's plain fare but there's plenty of it.

MRS. O'BRIEN. (*Returning with bread in one hand and two pairs of torn trousers in the other.*) Johnny, I found these in the other room. Not the same color, but they're sturdy and warm. (*Holds up one pair of blue trousers and one pair of yellow.*) William, here, tore one leg of the yellow pair—and Mark caught the blue ones on his scythe. But there's one good leg in each; so after dinner I'm going to make you some pants out of both of them!
(*All laugh and begin to eat heartily, as the* CURTAINS *close.*)

SCENE TWO

THERE is no change in scene, except that the candles are not lighted; the table has been cleared; and, if possible, the stage is a little brighter. JOHNNY *is standing in the middle of the room, clad in his new pied trousers. The* FAMILY *is gathered about him.*

❖　❖　❖　❖

ANNOUNCER. It is the next morning. Mrs. O'Brien made Johnny the blue and yellow trousers, and he is ready to continue his journey. All of them urge him to stay longer, and it seems as if he is tempted to do so.

(ANNOUNCER *leaves stage, and* CURTAINS *open to show scene described above.*)

JOHNNY.   Well, ma'am, no one will take me for a tramp now.

EMILY.   (*Going into a gale of laughter.*)   They look so funny, Mamma!

MRS. O'BRIEN.   They are all right, aren't they, Johnny?

JOHNNY.   Of course they are.   Just the thing!   With a good night's sleep, two hearty meals, and a clean suit of clothes— why, I could set out for Oregon!

MARK.   You know, Johnny, I've been wondering whether you wouldn't like to settle down and farm your own piece of land now?   You're not getting any younger, and there are a few acres here I'd like you to have.   Guess my ideas were too big when I cleared them—can't keep 'em all going.

WILLIAM.   (*Eagerly.*)   We'd all help you, Johnny.   After what you've done for the folks around here, it'd be a pleasure to get you settled on your own place.

JOHNNY.   Well, say, you're right kind to think of it.

MRS. O'BRIEN.   You could grow orchards for yourself, Johnny.   Wouldn't it be fine to gather in what you'd planted?

JOHNNY.   Well, ma'am, I can say truthfully it would.   But I don't know.   I never aimed to be a settler.

MARK.   But you are one, Johnny.   Just coming out here and planting trees where there weren't any—that's settling.

WILLIAM.   You could go on planting, sir—only you'd have your own fireplace at night to come back to.

JOHNNY.   Well, I—I don't know when I've seen a place I'd rather stay in.

EMILY.   Oh, please, Mr. Appleseed!

MARY.   Do live here!   Then we could see you often.

GEORGE.   But he wouldn't ever be going to Pittsburgh again!

MARY.   Sh!   George!   We'd rather have Mr. Appleseed.

GEORGE.   Oh, sure!   Won't you stay, sir?

JOHNNY.   You're making it awful hard for me to refuse.   It's true, I'm not so young any more, and the idea of a good bed every night isn't such a bad one . . .

MARY. He's going to do it! He's going to stay!

MARK. How about it, Johnny?

JOHNNY. Well, I—you better give me a little time to think. I don't know but what I might . . .
  (*Just then there is a* KNOCK *at the door. It is* CY *with a basket of apples on his arm.*)

MRS. O'BRIEN. Go to the door, Emily. (EMILY *does so.*) Oh, it's Cy!

CY. Look what I found on my place, Mark! Apples! Bushels of them! My first crop!

MARK. (*Examining them.*) Say! They're all right! Where did they come from?

CY. The far end of my property. I hadn't been all the way down—and when I walked there this morning, a whole orchard was just waiting to be picked. (*Suddenly an idea comes to him, and he looks at* JOHNNY.) Why, say, you wouldn't—*you* didn't plant 'em?

JOHNNY. (*Smiles at him.*) I did, son. Years ago. It was on one of my first trips across this part of the country. So they all grew into trees, eh?

CY. Oh, yes, sir! Beautiful trees! Why, it almost gives me the courage to send for my wife right now. It doesn't somehow look like such a long job with an orchard already bearing fruit like this.
  (*He passes apples around.*)

JOHNNY. (*As he takes one.*) Yes, they're good apples, all right. (*Pauses, and then turns to* MARK.) You know, Mark, I kind of think this is the answer to your question. I couldn't settle down and farm here. Why, my work is planting apple trees! Just seeing this man come in with his arms full of them makes me realize that this is my real job. And I've got to keep on doing it.

MARK. But you've planted so many of them, Johnny. Nobody else in this country has laid out the orchards you have. Why don't you stop now and take a rest?

JOHNNY. No, Mark. You don't understand. I'm an old man, but I'm not a farmer—or a settler, either. When I left Boston years ago as a young fellow, it was to plant apples all through the wilderness. That's my life, just like yours is building a barn and raising crops. Having people pleased with them is all the payment I want.

(*There is a pause.*)

MRS. O'BRIEN. I understand, Johnny. I don't think you'd ever be happy settling down in one place.

JOHNNY. I wouldn't, ma'am, and that's a fact. Why, this whole land is mine to plant trees on. People for miles and miles around are my neighbors. Even the animals and birds in the forest are my friends. Maybe some folks call me a tramp—I don't know. But it's my life, Mark; and it's the way I like it.

CY. (*Stepping up to shake his hand.*) Well, sir, you have my thanks for one orchard already growing in a new land.

MARK. And you have our thanks, too, for all the help you've been to us in making this farm the place it is.

JOHNNY. Well, you see, then, why I have to be going along?

MARK. (*Shakes* JOHNNY'S *hand.*) And good luck to you! We'll be looking for you when you come back this way. Good-by, Jonathan Chapman!

JOHNNY. No—just "Johnny Appleseed."

(*He goes out quickly, as they all stand looking affectionately after him. The* CURTAINS *close.*)

Production Notes

PROPERTIES:

table	large basket of apples
small pile of wood	plate of corn bread
2 long benches	candles
bowls	pitcher of milk
4 chairs	bowl of stew
kettle	pair of blue trousers and pair
cupboard	of yellow trousers
chest	little doll ⎫
plates, cups, etc.	book ⎬ in Johnny's
fireplace	little cart ⎪ knapsack
	colored kerchief ⎭

COSTUMES:

The men wear long, rather tight-fitting trousers, rough sack coats, white shirts with string ties, and boots or heavy shoes. Materials are dull in color and of coarse homespun weave.

The women wear dresses with long full skirts, rather high waists and tight bodices. The shoulders are sloping, and shawls are worn over them. Colors are somber. Hair is arranged simply, with middle part, and bun at the neck. There was great simplicity in the middle of the century, particularly in the clothing of the settlers.

Children's costumes were like their elders' in every respect.

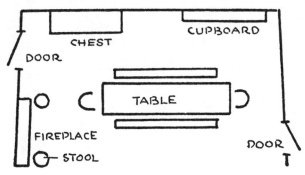

CLEVER MARYA AND THE CZAR

A Russian Legend

WIT AND SUSPENSE are the ingredients here in a dramatization of the Russian legend about a clever peasant girl who twice solves three of the Czar's riddles. The first three riddles were answered by Marya to settle a dispute over a calf, but she solves the second three to prove her wisdom—and as a result, is chosen by the Czar to be his wife.

15

CHARACTERS

MARYA, *the peasant's daughter*

YEGOR, *her father*

IVAN, *her uncle*

MARCO
FEODOR } *the rich cousins*

THE CZAR

*TWO BOYARDS

A PEASANT WOMAN

ATTENDANTS AND NOBLEMEN, *any number*

STORY TELLER

*Boyards were members of a Russian aristocratic order, next to ruling princes. The rank was abolished by Peter the Great.

SCENE 1: *On the road near the village; one morning.*

SCENE 2: *The Czar's palace; the next day.*

SCENE 3: *The same; the next day.*

CLEVER MARYA AND THE CZAR

SCENE ONE

THIS SCENE can be played either in front of the curtain or on a bare stage suggesting a road. If scenery is used, there should be trees, bushes, and rocks; however, none is needed so far as the action is concerned, and the scene change will therefore be accomplished more easily without these pieces.

❖   ❖   ❖   ❖

STORY TELLER. (*Coming to front of stage, bowing, and introducing the legend.*) This legend, or "skazka," of *Clever Marya and the Czar* takes place many years ago in old Russia. There were once two brothers—one a rich farmer, and the other a poor peasant. A year before our story begins, the rich brother had given his niece, the poor man's daughter, a sickly young cow. Now he is told that the young girl has taken such good care of the animal that it has grown healthy and strong, and even has borne a fine calf! The characters who appear in this tale are Ivan, the rich brother; Yegor, the poor peasant; Marya, his daughter; Marco and Feodor, cousins; the Czar and his boyards; attendants and persons in the court. There are three scenes; the first takes place on a road near the village.

(STORY TELLER *bows and goes off. The* CURTAINS *open on Scene One.* IVAN, *his two sons*—MARCO *and* FEODOR —*and* YEGOR, *and his daughter,* MARYA, *are talking together in the road.*)

MARCO. There! You see, Father? She admits it is true! Our cousin has tended the heifer you gave her until it is healthy and strong.

FEODOR. And there is now a calf to make her rich! Two animals where a year ago there were none!

IVAN. Is it true what they say, Marya?

17

MARYA. (*To her uncle, brightly.*) Yes, indeed, Uncle. If you come to our cottage, I will show you how well they are doing.

YEGOR. My daughter has taken good care of your gift, brother Ivan. Many a night she has sat up with the little one, feeding and keeping it warm on a soft bed of straw. And now, thanks to you, she is the owner of both a cow and a calf.

MARCO. (*To his father.*) But you did not give her the calf, Father.

FEODOR. (*To his father.*) Tell her that only the heifer is hers. You did not mean her to keep its young.

IVAN. My sons are right, Marya. A year ago I gave you the cow, and I am pleased with the care you have shown it. But I did not say anything about keeping the calves. They should belong to me.

MARYA. But, Uncle, surely if my own cow has a calf, it is mine!

YEGOR. My daughter is right, brother Ivan. Since you said nothing about the calf then, you can make no claim now.

FEODOR. But your daughter has *one* fine healthy cow! Why must she be greedy for more?

MARCO. If it were not for our father, she would have none at all!

MARYA. When you gave me the cow, Uncle, you did not expect it to live. "Take her," you said to me. "If you can pull her through the long winter, she is yours." Very well. I have worked hard to save her life. And now that I have done so, I deserve whatever profit she brings.

IVAN. (*Annoyed with her.*) You are a headstrong girl, Marya. But it is easy to see how you come by it. Your father before you is obstinate.

YEGOR. (*Growing angry also.*) In this matter, yes, Brother Ivan! We will not give you the calf! Why, your barn is filled with fat cattle! What is one more?

FEODOR. He is after your pity now, Father.

MARCO. Crafty one! (*To* YEGOR.) So that is how you get along in the world! Why do you not work as our father does? He has made his wealth for himself.

IVAN. Yegor, I demand that you give me that calf!

YEGOR. And I refuse to obey you, my Brother! The calf is ours by all rights!

IVAN. (*Shouting at him.*) Must I take this to the court?

YEGOR. (*Shouting back.*) You will get nowhere if you do! There is no law which says that the calf is yours!

MARCO. (*Angry now.*) Show them, Father! Let us take this to the Czar!

FEODOR. Yes, they will have to do as he says!

MARYA. (*Tossing her head.*) Ask whom you will! I am going back to our cottage and tend to my calf!
(*She walks past them and out R.*)

IVAN. (*Shaking his fist after her angrily.*) We shall see, my girl, how much longer that calf is yours! (*To his sons.*) Come, Marco, Feodor! Let us go to the Czar!
(*At this moment, the* CZAR *and his two* BOYARDS *enter from L. They overhear the last statement and are taken aback.*)

CZAR. (*To his* BOYARDS.) Let us stop here a moment. (*To* IVAN.) What is it you would take to your Czar?

IVAN. (*Also startled, but bowing low and respectfully.*) Oh, Czar, it is nothing. Only an argument I was having with my brother, here.
(YEGOR *also bows at the mention of his name.*)

CZAR. But you mentioned my name. What have I to do with your quarrel?

FIRST BOYARD. Perhaps they would like you to help them.

SECOND BOYARD. Or settle some point of the law.

CZAR. Is that it?

IVAN. (*Bowing again.*) That is it, O Czar. You see, my brother and I——

19

YEGOR. (*Bowing.*) I have a daughter, O Czar——

CZAR. (*Interrupting.*) Very well. You may each tell your story. I do not know that I can help you, but I promise to listen. Go ahead.

(*The* CZAR *crosses his arms, and stands waiting for the story.*)

IVAN. (*Glancing first at* YEGOR, *then beginning.*) Well, you see—my brother, here, has a daughter. Last winter when they were so poor, I gave her a cow. Now, the heifer has brought forth a calf, and the girl insists upon keeping it for herself. I say she owns only the cow. The calf should be mine.

(IVAN *stops and stands respectfully waiting for the* CZAR *to reply. But instead he nods to* YEGOR.)

CZAR. And your side of the argument, my friend?

YEGOR. It is true, what he says. But the cow he gave my Marya, O Czar, was a thin, sickly one. He had not thought it would live. All the long winter she cared for it until it grew healthy and strong. And now that its calf has been born, we think it is ours to keep.

CZAR. (*Nods and looks over at* MARCO *and* FEODOR.) And these two lads—who are they?

IVAN. My sons, O Czar. They have been here all the time and will swear I am telling the truth.

CZAR. I do not doubt your story. But I am not yet sure of the answer. (*Turning now to* YEGOR.) And your daughter, my friend—where is she?

YEGOR. She has gone home to take care of the calf.

CZAR. I see. (*He pauses a moment, then continues.*) I think I shall not settle this right away. Instead, I shall ask you three riddles. You will appear at my palace tomorrow morning with the answers to each.

IVAN. (*Greedily.*) But which of us gets the calf? I do not understand.

CZAR. He who answers best all three of the riddles. That

one will get both the calf and the cow. The other will have learned his lesson.

IVAN. (*Sullenly.*) Very well, then.

YEGOR. As you say, O Czar.

CZAR. Good! Then here is the first question: "What is the swiftest thing in the world?" (*There is a pause as the* BROTHERS *think and put it away in their minds.*) Next: "What of all things on this earth is the fattest?" (*There is another pause as they think again.*) And third: "In all life, what thing is most pleasant?" (*There is a third pause. Both* BROTHERS *look bewildered and a bit desperate.*) Now then, you have been given three riddles. You will come before me in the morning with your answers. To him whose answers are the best, I will grant my decision. (*To his* BOYARDS.) Come, boyards, let us continue our walk through the village.

(*The* CZAR *and his* BOYARDS *move off right, as the* BROTHERS *and the two* SONS *bow low. Then they stand looking helplessly at each other as the* CURTAINS *close.*)

SCENE TWO

THIS SCENE takes place in the CZAR'S *palace. Two thrones are in the center of the stage, and there may be hangings or other richly colored decorations in the room. There is no other furniture needed so far as the action is concerned, but an impression of richness and elegance will add to the atmosphere. As the curtains open, the* CZAR *is seated on one throne; the other is empty. His* BOYARDS, *a* PEASANT WOMAN, *and other* ATTENDANTS *are all in the room*

❖ ❖ ❖ ❖

STORY TELLER. It is the next morning in the palace. The Czar is having audience with his people, and Ivan and Yegor are next to appear.

(*He bows, goes off, and the* CURTAINS *open.*)

21

CZAR. (*To a* PEASANT WOMAN *who is standing before him.*)
And you say, my good woman, that someone has stolen the
cabbages from your garden?

WOMAN. Yes, O Czar! A week ago there were twenty of
them. And this morning one only is left! Little fathers!
How I cared for those plants! They were ready for market
—and now I have nothing to sell.

CZAR. On what do you live, my good woman?

WOMAN. On my garden, O Czar. I sell what I raise there.

CZAR. (*To the* BOYARD *nearest him.*) Boyard, go to our
storehouse and get her as many cabbages as she lost. And
give her the largest you find!

FIRST BOYARD. Yes, O Czar. I obey you at once.
(*He bows and leaves by the door L.*)

WOMAN. (*Bowing low.*) Oh, thank you! Now I can buy
flour and black bread for the month!

CZAR. Let us know if you are robbed again. You may go.
(*She backs from the room, gratefully, and leaves by the
door L. The* CZAR *then calls to the* BOYARD *who is standing near the entrance.*)

CZAR. And now you may summon the next.

BOYARD. (*Nods and steps out for* IVAN *and* YEGOR.) Yes,
master.
(IVAN *and* YEGOR *walk timidly toward the throne, then
bow fearfully.*)

CZAR. It's the two brothers who were arguing over the calf!

IVAN. Yes, O Czar.

YEGOR. You asked us to come.

CZAR. I remember. You were given three riddles to guess.
Have you thought of the answers?

IVAN. (*Boastfully.*) All night, O Czar, I have thought and
thought. And now I am ready.

CZAR. (*Turning to* YEGOR.) And you, O Peasant?

22

YEGOR. I, too, have thought, and await your decision.

CZAR. Very well, then. The first of the riddles: "What of all things in the world is most swift?"

(*He looks at* IVAN, *who replies with assurance.*)

IVAN. My horse, O Czar. In my stable is a mare that nothing can pass. Of all running things, she must be the most swift.

(*The* CZAR *laughs and looks at* YEGOR.)

CZAR. And your answer to this?

YEGOR. O Czar, I believe there is nothing so swift as our thoughts as they pass through our heads.

CZAR. (*Both astonished and pleased at the reply.*) Good, O Peasant! And now for the second: "What of all things on this earth is most fat?"

(*Again he looks first at* IVAN, *who answers less assuredly this time.*)

IVAN. O Czar, in my sty is a hog. She has won seven prizes! Surely nothing in the world can be half so fat!

(*The* CZAR *laughs more loudly than before; then he turns to* YEGOR.)

CZAR. And what is your reply to this riddle?

YEGOR. (*With a slight hesitation.*) Of all things on this earth, O Czar, there is nothing to compare with the fat of the land.

CZAR. (*Again astonished and more pleased than before.*) Well done, again, Peasant. And now for the third: "What is it in this world that's most pleasant?"

(*He turns to* IVAN, *who now appears diffident and insecure.*)

IVAN. O Czar, I had thought that a woman, soft-spoken and kind, is of all things the most pleasant.

(*The* CZAR *laughs loud and long, and turns for a third time to* YEGOR.)

CZAR. And have you an answer to this one, too?

YEGOR. Yes, O Czar. The most pleasant thing in this earth is sound sleep. For in it our troubles and poverty are forgotten.

CZAR. (*Delighted with him once more.*) Right three times, Peasant! How did you think of these answers?

YEGOR. It was not I who thought of them, O Czar, but my daughter, Marya. I could have done no better than he. (*Nodding to* IVAN, *who glares at him.*) Each one I put to her first, and each one she answered.

CZAR. You are honest, old man. And your daughter has wisdom. To you go the calf and the cow.

YEGOR. (*Humbly.*) Thank you! Thank you, O Czar!

CZAR. (*To* IVAN.) You, my foolish one, are dismissed. But the next time you are asked, look beyond that rich farm for your answers.

(IVAN *bows with a bad grace and departs by door L. Then the* CZAR *turns back to* YEGOR.)

CZAR. As for you, I am not yet done. I should like to see this daughter of yours, but I shall send her a riddle first that I doubt even she can guess.

YEGOR. I will tell her, O Czar.

CZAR. Then ask her to appear before me tomorrow—neither on foot nor on horseback, neither dressed nor undressed, and bearing with her a gift that I cannot return.

YEGOR. She will be here tomorrow, O Czar, though I cannot think how she will answer this riddle.

CZAR. We shall find out how clever she is. Go, my good man. You have won your argument, but there is a task still to be done.

(YEGOR *bows low and leaves, shaking his head sadly as he goes. On this, the* CURTAINS *close.*)

SCENE THREE

*A*S THE CURTAINS *open, the* CZAR *is seated on his throne with* ONE BOYARD *by his side, and the* OTHER *near the* *door.* The LADIES *and* GENTLEMEN *of the court are all eagerly waiting for* MARYA.

❖   ❖   ❖   ❖

STORY TELLER. It is morning of the next day, and Marya is to appear before the Czar. Old Yegor has come with her, and all the palace is awaiting her reply to this most difficult of all riddles.

(*He bows and goes off.* CURTAINS *open.*)

CZAR. (*Impatiently, to the* BOYARD *nearest him.*) Is it not time for the peasant's daughter to appear?

FIRST BOYARD. It is still early, O Czar. And they are poor folk who must walk to the village.

SECOND BOYARD. (*By the door.*) I hear a disturbance below. Perhaps they are on their way up here now.

(*Sound of* LAUGHING *outside.*)

CZAR. Go and see. If it is, show them in. (BOYARD *leaves.*) Now, we shall see if this Marya is as clever as they say.

(*At this moment, the* BOYARD *appears in the doorway, followed by* YEGOR, *who is carrying* MARYA *on his back. She is dressed in yards of bright material. He moves slowly to the throne, and shouts of laughter go up from the court.*)

CZAR. Silence! What is the meaning of this?

(MARYA *dismounts easily, and bows gracefully before the* CZAR. *In spite of her apparel, she is lovely and poised.*)

MARYA. O Czar, I have come as you asked: "Neither on foot nor on horseback"—but carried in this way by my father; "neither dressed nor undressed"—but wrapped in yards of this cloth; and "bearing with me a gift which you cannot return." That gift is the thanks in my heart for restoring our cow and her calf. Now, surely, I have answered your riddle.

CZAR. (*More delighted with her than he had been with her father the day before.*) Marya, you are wiser even than I

25

had hoped! For mixed with your wisdom is humor. But you must know why I asked you to come here. I have long sought a wife who would sit on this throne by my side. But in all my czardom there has been no woman with beauty and cleverness both. You, Marya, are the one for whom I've been hunting. And I ask you to become my bride.

(*There is a pause; then* MARYA *speaks.*)

MARYA. I should be foolish, O Czar, if I did not accept one so handsome and just.

CZAR. (*Rises and smiles as he speaks.*) At last, my people, I have found a wife who is clever as well as beautiful. She will be a joy in the court when I am here—and a wise ruler in my absence. (*Turning to* YEGOR, *who is standing to one side.*) As for you, my friend, you have shown yourself honest and humble. For this, you will dwell in the palace the rest of your life. You need not part from your daughter, and your days of hard work are now done.

YEGOR. It is too much, O Czar!

MARYA. (*Turning to the old man, joyfully.*) Little Father, little Father! Our poverty is over at last!

CZAR. (*Smiling at him, too.*) This court is your home. Pray be welcome. (*Then he turns to* MARYA *and takes her by the hand.*) You, Marya, take your place by my side. Tomorrow you will reign as Czarina!

(*They sit together, and the entire court takes up the cry.*)

ALL. Long live the Czar! Long live his Czarina!

(*There is delighted shouting as the* CURTAINS *close.*)

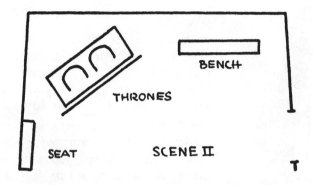

CLEVER MARYA AND THE CZAR

Production Notes

FURNISHINGS:
   Two thrones
   Two or three other chairs or benches
   Bright-colored hangings

COSTUMES:

MARYA and the PEASANT WOMAN wear full skirts with tight bodices, or full skirts and peasant blouses with aprons. Clothing is bright-colored and embroidered. Bright babushkas are worn also.

WOMEN OF THE COURT wear elaborate, brightly colored gowns of rich materials, with tight bodices, low necklines, and long full skirts. Hair is long and flowing or braided and topped with headdresses.

The PEASANT MEN wear simple tunics falling almost to the knees, and belted in at the waist. Full trousers are worn with boots or heavy lacing up the legs. Colors are dull; and materials, coarse.

The MEN OF THE COURT wear shorter tunics. They are less full and of brighter, richer fabrics. They are embroidered and decorated with elaborate designs. Contrasting sleeves are wide and generous at the shoulders. They wear decorative belts and well-polished boots. The Czar has a crown. Other noblemen have swords.

THE COINS OF LIN FOO

A Chinese Legend

HOW A WISE MAGISTRATE once discovered a thief is told in this dramatization of an ancient Chinese legend. It is a tale of wit and wisdom, using as background a country village and the peasants who dwell in it. The boy, Lin Foo, after selling fritters at the market, foolishly puts the money he has earned underneath a stone by the roadside. When he returns several hours later and finds the money gone, he is overcome with despair. A wise magistrate passing by hears his cries, and promises to solve the mystery and restore the lost coins. This he does the next morning at a trial in which he places the stone under arrest. This absurd device enables him to discover the real thief, and the little Lin Foo is repaid. There is humor and charm in the unfolding of this ancient tale.

CHARACTERS

THE CHORUS, *a boy, dignified, elaborately dressed*

PROPERTY MAN, *inconspicuous in black, casual*

AN LI, *the magistrate, commanding respect*

LIN FOO, *the boy, humble, poorly dressed*

WING SOONG, *the widow, poorly dressed, hard-working*

TWO ATTENDANTS, *for the magistrate*

VILLAGERS, *any number, three who speak*

THE ORCHESTRA, *four or five*

SCENE 1: *The doorway to Wing Soong's cottage, and the road.*

SCENE 2: *The road to the village.*

SCENE 3: *The same.*

THE COINS OF LIN FOO

*T*HE STAGE *is bare, except for a table and chair U.L., where the* PROPERTY MAN *sits. All properties to be used in the play are here and are distributed at the appropriate times. There are two doors—the left one for entrances, and the right one for exits. Four or five* MUSICIANS, *if they are used, sit against the rear wall, playing when there is no dialogue going on, increasing their din when excitement is high, and becoming quiet during important scenes. One of them must have a gong which he strikes, in Chinese tradition, to indicate the end of a scene.*

The CHORUS *gives his opening speech before the curtain. Then he bows graciously and leaves. When the* CURTAINS *are open,* WING SOONG *has taken her place D.R.*

❖ ❖ ❖ ❖

CHORUS. (*Walking in with great dignity, and going to the center of the stage where he bows three times.*) Most honored ladies and gentlemen, there is an ancient legend told in China of The Magistrate and the Stone. Our players this afternoon would like to perform it for you if we may have your most gracious permission. (*He bows again, waits a moment, then goes on.*) It is my humble privilege to introduce to you the characters who appear in this story. First in importance is the great magistrate, An Li. It is said that he has never failed to solve a case brought before him, and the people all praise his wisdom and judgment. (AN LI *enters, crosses to the middle of the stage, bows courteously, then goes off on the other side. The* CHORUS *continues.*) In a certain small village in the state of Tsin, there lives a humble widow, Wing Soong, and her only son, the little Lin Foo. Though her husband was a thrifty farmer, with rice fields of his own, drought and hard times have come, forcing the good Wing Soong to sell the land and earn a living for herself and her son. This she does by making

31

fritters to sell on market days. Little Lin Foo takes the fritters each week in his basket, returning at night with the money from their sale.

(*Announcing.*) The woman, Wing Soong. (*She walks to the center of the stage.*) And her son, the little Lin Foo.

(*He joins her. Both bow and go out on the other side.*)

Others whom you will see in the play are the two attendants of the good magistrate. (ATTENDANTS *come forward together, bow, and leave briskly.*) The Property Man, who will set the stage and hand the actors the properties they need.

(PROPERTY MAN *saunters forth, bows casually, and strolls off again in a bored manner.*) And all of the village folk, who are called in the last scene to be witnesses at the trial. I shall not ask them to step forward now, for our patient audience will become weary of so many introductions.

(The CHORUS *walks to a spot D.R.*) It is morning. The pear trees are in blossom. Over here we have the humble cottage of Wing Soong, where the poor widow is just finishing her fritters for the market.

(*The* CHORUS *claps his hands, bows, goes off. The* CURTAINS *open. A gong is struck, and the* MUSICIANS *begin to play. They play undisturbed a moment while the* PROPERTY MAN *quietly carries a large basket over to* WING SOONG, *then returns to his chair. The* MUSIC *subsides.*)

WING SOONG. Little Lin Foo! (*Calls again.*) Little Lin Foo!

LIN FOO. (*He crosses the stage to her.*) Yes, my Mother.

WING SOONG. It is time now to take the basket of fritters to the market place. It is said they are having a fair in the village today; so I have made twice as many for you to sell.

LIN FOO. Good Mother, then may I walk around a bit before coming home? I should like to see the wares on the tables,

32

the flags of our country, and the little, carved, wooden dragons and birds.

WING SOONG. Of course, my Son. Just mind you keep the money safe, and do not stay so long in the village that it grows dark on your journey home.

LIN FOO. I shall take care of the money, Mother; and you will see me coming through the gate before the first flowers have closed their petals for the night.

WING SOONG. Then be off, little Son. For the way is long, and already the village will be crowded with the farmers and their carts.

LIN FOO. Good-by, Mother.

(*He starts out, makes a complete circle around the stage to indicate traveling a great distance, then leaves at R.*)

WING SOONG. (*With a sigh.*) How I wish that I might someday earn enough money to educate the little Lin Foo, that he might grow up to be a scholar instead of a peasant lad, selling his wares at the market.

(*She wipes her eyes, then goes off D.R. The* PROPERTY MAN *gets the stool she has been sitting on, takes it to his table, and the* GONG *is struck. The curtains are pulled only twice in the play—at the beginning and at the end. Otherwise, it is not necessary, since the* CHORUS *marks the division between scenes, and it is traditional for the stage manager to change properties in full view of the audience.*)

SCENE TWO

CHORUS. (*Comes on again, bows low, and speaks.*) The little Lin Foo spent a happy and profitable day in the village. First he sold his basket of fritters and put the money in his trousers' pocket. Indeed, he had no trouble at all in selling the fritters, for the humble Wing Soong was known throughout the village for her fine cooking and fair bargains. The little lad went from booth to booth, finally deciding that the safest place for his money was under a stone near the entrance to the town. Then he could run and play to his heart's content, with no fear of the coins' slipping out of his pocket and rolling away in the dust. So, carefully he placed them there, and joined some village boys he knew. Finally it was time to go home. He bade his friends farewell, and went to the stone under which he had hidden his money.

(CHORUS *bows and leaves. A* GONG *strikes. The* PROP-ERTY MAN *places a stone in the center of the stage, saunters back to his chair, and sits. The* ORCHESTRA *plays briefly, then subsides as* LIN FOO *enters.*)

LIN FOO. (*Coming in at L. and going to the stone.*) Now to put the money back in my pocket and go home before it is dark. (*He stoops and looks, but the money is not there.*) Oh, my money! Where is it? All the coins that I put here are gone! Someone has stolen them while I played in the village. What will my mother, Wing Soong, do? She used all the money in our old stone crock to buy rice for the fritters! Oh dear, oh dear!

(*He sits down and weeps. While he is sitting there, the magistrate,* AN LI, *comes in from L., accompanied by his* TWO ATTENDANTS.)

AN LI. Why are you weeping, my boy?

LIN FOO. Oh, Master, I am a poor boy whose mother makes fritters to sell on market day. She entrusted me to bring home the money which I placed under this stone for safe-keeping. When I came to get it just now, I found it had been stolen. And so I have neither money nor fritters to take back with me!

AN LI. Have you a father, little son?

LIN FOO. Oh, no, sir. There are just the two of us—my mother, Wing Soong, and I, who am called Lin Foo. We are very poor and must have what we earn at the market to live.

AN LI. Did you put the money well out of sight?

LIN FOO. Oh, yes, honored sir. No one could possibly have seen it.

AN LI. (*Pointing to it.*) Is this the stone?

LIN FOO. It is, Your Honor.

AN LI. (*To his* ATTENDANTS.) Then arrest this stone! You, my boy, may now go home. But don't fail to come back to this spot tomorrow morning. I shall try to get your money back for you.

LIN FOO. Yes, sir! Indeed, I shall!

AN LI. Now then, run along. It's growing late, and your mother will be worried.

LIN FOO. Oh, thank you! I shall be here in the morning. Good-by, Master.
    (*He runs in a circle, and out on the opposite side, which is D.R. The* MAGISTRATE *speaks to his* ATTENDANTS.)

AN LI. Summon all the villagers who were at the fair today, to be present tomorrow morning. Let them be witnesses at the trial of this stone.

ATTENDANT. Yes, Your Honor.

AN LI. Bring with you also the magistrate's table and chair, two stout bamboo sticks, and a large stone jar.

ATTENDANT. Yes, Your Honor.

AN LI. That is all, then. You are dismissed.
    (ATTENDANTS *bow low, and leave the stage U.R.* AN LI *steps forward and addresses the audience.*)
I have been honored with the title, Magistrate, of this district. Since I have been in office, I have tried to perform my duties with justice and wisdom. This case is a most difficult one— for to prosecute a stone is impossible, and I am not yet certain as to how I shall find the stolen money for the poor Lin Foo and his widowed mother. In the morning I shall be watched by a hundred eyes! I must go home now to

meditate upon this case. Tomorrow, most distinguished audience, we meet again.

(*He bows low, goes off R., and the* GONG *is struck.*)

SCENE THREE

CHORUS. (*Coming on again and bowing.*) It is the following day, and Wing Soong and her son have already left their cottage for the trial of the stone. As the Magistrate commanded, the attendants have summoned all the villagers from the market place to act as witnesses. With your kind approval, ladies and gentlemen, the trial is about to begin.

(*He bows, goes off, and the* GONG *is sounded. The* OR-CHESTRA *is playing; and the* PROPERTY MAN *is moving about, putting the stone in place, then the table and chair, and last of all, the bamboo sticks and jar. Into the jar, the* PROPERTY MAN *pours water. He retires to his table, where he is only occasionally interested in the proceedings. The* PEOPLE *begin to enter and stand about in small groups. A few of them talk.* WING SOONG *and* LIN FOO *are in the crowd.*)

FIRST VILLAGER. They say the great An Li has sentenced a stone for the theft of some money.

SECOND VILLAGER. Yes. Some say he has lost his wits from so much study of the law.

THIRD VILLAGER. He has summoned all of us here to help him try the case.

FIRST VILLAGER. Let us see what he plans to do. Perhaps there is reason for his strange course.

SECOND VILLAGER. I think his mind is affected, and this is the proof of it.

(AN LI *and his* TWO ATTENDANTS *enter U.L., and the* GONG *is struck. There is much ceremony, as* AN LI *takes his place at the table, with the* ATTENDANTS *standing on each side of him.*)

36

THIRD VILLAGER. (*To his neighbor.*) He looks all right. But one can never tell from appearances.

SECOND VILLAGER. Sh! They are about to speak.

AN LI. (*Bows and sits.*) I have called all of you together this morning, my good friends, to act as witnesses at the trial of a stone. (*The* CROWD *murmurs.*) Silence! Is the boy, Lin Foo, present?

LIN FOO. (*Stepping forward bashfully.*) He is, Your Honor.

AN LI. And his mother, the widow, Wing Soong?

WING SOONG. (*Stepping forward.*) She is, Your Honor.

AN LI. Did you, Wing Soong, give your son a basket of fritters to sell at the fair yesterday?

WING SOONG Yes, Your Honor.

AN LI. And was the money for those fritters stolen from under the stone where he had hidden it?

WING SOONG. Oh, yes, Your Honor.

AN LI. (*Turning to the boy.*) Was it this stone that stole the coins? (*As he points to it, there is a* RIPPLE *of* AMUSEMENT *from the crowd.*) Quiet!

LIN FOO. Yes, Your Honor.

AN LI. (*Turning to his* ATTENDANTS.) Then will you strike the stone fifty times with the bamboo sticks?
　　(*Now the* PEOPLE *laugh loudly, tapping their heads and showing ridicule, as the* ATTENDANTS *step forward and begin beating the stone.*)

AN LI. (*Suddenly shouting.*) Silence! You are showing contempt for this court! Each one of you shall be fined twenty li, which you will toss into this jar!
　　(*They are sobered as they file past the jar in a circle and drop in their coins. As the last man drops his in, the* MAGISTRATE *jumps up and shouts out.*)
Arrest this man! He is the thief!
　　(*There is a murmur of excitement and bewilderment.*)

FIRST VILLAGER. How does he know?

SECOND VILLAGER. The thief? Is he really the thief?

THIRD VILLAGER. He cannot tell!
(*There is general* HUBBUB *of exclamations among the crowd.*)

AN LI. (*Picking up the jar, which he brings forward, showing it to the crowd.*) Do you see here? When this man dropped in his coin, these streaks of grease appeared on the surface of the water. Only *that* coin could have come from the basket that carried the fritters! (*To the* THIEF.) Where is the rest of the money?

THIEF. (*Pulling it unwillingly from his pocket.*) Here it is, Your Honor.

AN LI. Put it in the jar. (THIEF *does so.*) Take him away. (*The* ATTENDANTS *take him by both arms, and they go off U.R.*) The court is dismissed!
(*The* VILLAGERS *leave through both doors, expressing their amazement and respect for the magistrate's wisdom. All murmur softly until they are off the stage. Finally* AN LI *hands the jar to* WING SOONG.)

AN LI. There you are, my good woman. Your money is restored to you, and I hope your son has learned his lesson— never to leave things of value foolishly in such a spot as this, thus tempting the dishonest folk who pass by to steal them.

WING SOONG. (*Taking it gratefully.*) Oh, thank you, great Master. This humble servant now has twice as much money as the fritters would have brought.

AN LI. Then take it home and put it in safekeeping. (*Claps his hands to the* ATTENDANTS, *who have just returned from U.R.*) Attendants, let us depart!
(*They exit U.R. Both* WING SOONG *and* LIN FOO *bow low as they exit. They smile, sigh happily, and walk in a circle, and out in the direction of their cottage D.R. The* GONG *strikes; the* MUSICIANS *begin to play loudly; and the* CURTAINS *close.*)

Production Notes

PROPERTIES:

instruments for musicians
gong
basket of fritters
large stone (a cloth-covered imitation will be easier to handle)
table and chair
2 bamboo sticks
jar for water
pitcher of water (for Property Man to pour into jar)
coins (enough for each person in the crowd)

COSTUMES:

LIN FOO and all the village people wear knee-length tunics and long trousers of dull colors, and coarse materials. Blues and grays are generally used with no decoration or ornamentation. Soft slippers and coolie hats can be worn if desired.

The PROPERTY MAN wears the traditional black coat and trousers. He should be as plain and inconspicuous as possible.

WING SOONG and the village women have longer tunics than those worn by the men, trousers, and soft slippers. Women's clothing includes printed materials as well as plain colors. The hair is straight and drawn to a knot at the nape of the neck.

The MAGISTRATE'S coat is very long and ornate. The colors are bright, and gold embroidery is on the clothing. He also wears a round, mandarin cap.

STYLE OF PRODUCTION:

Since the Chinese manner of staging is one of great simplicity, the play can be done as easily in a classroom as upon a stage. There is an opportunity for studying Chinese customs, art, and clothing, if a social-studies unit is being prepared at this time. Children can easily design a simple screen or make tapestries, which will add color and atmosphere to the production. If Chinese costumes are available, they can be worn. On the other hand, because the theatre itself is so highly symbolic, the play can be performed with little or nothing in the way of scenery and costumes, leaving such details to be supplied by the imagination of the audience.

An orchestra of four or five children, who sit on the stage throughout, will give a flavor of the country and the time. Chinese music is not attempted, since it would be beyond the ability of young students. In the original production, the orchestra was simply instructed to "make a din." Popular or recognizable American music would be out of place, of course. Use of the Chinese pentatonic scale will give the effect.

Scene changes can be made very easily, as the Chorus acts as narrator; and the Property Man brings on and carries off the various items in full view of the audience.

WHO LAUGHS LAST?

A Polish Legend

ONE of the gayest of national legends comes to us from Poland. This dramatization tells of a jester, whose wits were thought dull; yet he played a merry prank which brought him a fortune and baffled a king. Although there are two settings— the palace and the cottage—neither calls for elaborate staging. The action and charm of the story itself are of primary interest; therefore scenery and costumes need not be stressed unless it seems worthwhile to do so. As an assembly play or a classroom project, *Who Laughs Last?* ought to be amusing, and not difficult to produce.

CHARACTERS

THE ANNOUNCER

KING JAN

THE QUEEN

MATENKO, *the Jester*

ELZUNIA, *his wife*

LORDS

LADIES

A BEGGAR

SCENE 1: *The palace.*

SCENE 2: *The cottage, several months later.*

SCENE 3: *The cottage, an hour later.*

WHO LAUGHS LAST?

SCENE ONE

FOR THE first scene, two large, ornate chairs (placed, preferably, on a small platform) should be located at R.C., facing D.L. A bench D.R. (optional) and another U.L. will complete the furniture requirements. Whatever can be added to give the room a regal appearance will be in order, although such embellishments are optional.

❖   ❖   ❖   ❖

ANNOUNCER. Many, many years ago when Poland was ruled by King Jan, there was a jester in the palace named Matenko. He had served a lifetime in the court, and for years had been the favorite clown. But in his old age, his joints became so stiff and his wits so dull that even the lords and ladies who loved him best yawned behind their handkerchiefs when he performed. They begged King Jan to dismiss him and get a new clown. The first scene is in the palace. The characters are the King, the Queen, Matenko, his good wife Elzunia, and the lords and ladies of the court.

(*He bows and goes off. As the* CURTAINS *open, all are laughing and talking together. The* KING *and* QUEEN *sit on their thrones.*)

FIRST LORD. (*Interrupting the conversations.*) Matenko! Matenko! Perform for us! Of what use is a jester who sleeps in his corner?

(*The other* LORDS *and* LADIES *take up the cry, ad libbing as follows:* "Yes, Matenko, come out! . . . Where are you? . . . " *etc.* MATENKO *hobbles out stiffly, tries to bow, but fails. He addresses the* KING.)

MATENKO. What is your will, Master?

KING. Some trick, if you please! We have had nothing but gossip in the court all morning.

43

MATENKO. (*Scratching his head.*) Yes . . . there was a joke
. . . . I had it a moment ago. . . . If you will be patient . . .
(*He goes into a study as he tries to recall it.*)

FIRST LORD. It must be good if you make us wait for it!

SECOND LORD. No doubt it will be like the last one—heard
a dozen times before! Where have your wits flown to,
Matenko?

THIRD LORD. Time was when one joke followed another so
quickly no one could keep up with you!

FIRST LORD. Never mind, old clown. By the time you have
thought of it, no one will be listening.

SECOND LORD. Your Majesty, why do you not get us a new
jester—one whose movements are active and whose jokes
will amuse us?

THIRD LORD. Matenko has had his day. Why not let him
spend his old age in some peaceful place where tricks are
not asked of him?

QUEEN. There is something in what they say, my lord. They
do not mean to be unkind; but look, how tired the old man
is! He is no longer happy in the palace.

KING. Perhaps you are right. Matenko has been in this
palace for fifty years. Longer than I, myself. He was my
father's jester. My first plaything was his old cap with the
bells.

MATENKO. (*Trying to spring up.*) I have it! Listen!
"Why is a morning in the palace like a day at the market?"
(*Looks about him.*)

LADIES. Oh, we have heard it before!

FIRST LORD. An old one, Matenko. (*To the* KING.) You
see, Your Majesty?

MATENKO. (*Bewildered.*) Have I told it before?

KING. Yes, my good Matenko, many times.

MATENKO. Then I must think of another. Wait . . .
(*Goes into another study.*)

KING. No, my faithful old clown. I have a better plan. For

a long time we have known that some day you would be leaving us, and I have had a cottage near the palace grounds prepared for you. I had not thought it would be so soon. But the place is ready; so put away your bright jester's clothes and become a citizen of Poland.

MATENKO. (*Astonished.*) A cottage for my own?

QUEEN. And for your good wife, Elzunia. Bring her in to us.

(*A* LADY IN WAITING *goes for her, and returns with a plump, jolly* OLD WOMAN.)

ELZUNIA. (*As she enters.*) You have sent for me, Your Highness?

QUEEN. Yes, Elzunia. The King has something to tell you.

ELZUNIA. I am in the midst of baking a big cake for Your Majesty's dinner, but I can stay for a minute.

KING. No, Elzunia. This time you are not to return to the kitchen. Let someone else finish the cake for you.

ELZUNIA. (*Alarmed.*) Someone else? Has Elzunia's hand with the pastry grown heavy in her old age?

(*Looks anxiously at the* KING.)

KING. No, Elzunia. No. But the time has come for you and Matenko to retire and enjoy your old age in the peace of your own home. I have bought a small cottage for you on the edge of the palace grounds, and today you shall move into it.

ELZUNIA. Oh, Your Majesty, it is too much! I had expected to die in your service.

QUEEN. Well, you shall not. You and Matenko have served faithfully for many years and deserve a good rest.

KING. There will be money for you to live on. But you must come to see us sometimes, even though we have a new jester.

MATENKO. (*Bewildered.*) Yes, Your Majesty. And thank you for your kindness.

KING. Will someone take them to their cottage at once? (*A* LORD *steps forward.*) Everything is ready for you. Good-by, Matenko!

MATENKO. (*Stumbling out the door after the* LORD.) Good-by, Your Majesty.

ELZUNIA. You have been good to us!

QUEEN. No better than you deserve. Good-by, Elzunia! (*There is a confusion of voices, as the* LORDS *and* LADIES *call,* "*Good-by! Good luck, Matenko!*" *etc. And the* CURTAINS *close.*)

SCENE TWO

$\mathcal{F}$OR THIS SCENE, *the benches and throne chairs have been removed. A small table, with plain chairs R. and L. of it, is placed slightly below C. A small cupboard against the wall L. completes the necessary requirements for the humble cottage of Matenko and Elzunia.*

❖   ❖   ❖   ❖

ANNOUNCER. Several months have passed. King Jan has found a new jester who pleases the lords and ladies mightily. Poor Matenko and his wife are all but forgotten. The King and Queen have not even remembered to send the money they promised, to keep up the cottage and buy food. The next scene is in the old couple's kitchen, where we find the jester and his wife wondering how they can get themselves some kind of living.

(*As the* CURTAINS *open, the* JESTER *and his* WIFE *are sitting despondently at the empty table.*)

MATENKO. Poor Elzunia! To end your days in hunger and want.

ELZUNIA. Poor Matenko! Once the favorite clown in His Majesty's service—and now no richer than a beggar!

MATENKO. If only I could find work. But no one will hire an old man who knows nothing except playing the fool!

ELZUNIA. If only I could have the food that is wasted in one day at the palace! It would be enough for us to live on for a month.

MATENKO. Why do you suppose the King has never sent so much as one gold piece to us since we left?

ELZUNIA. Perhaps he has forgotten us. They say there is a new jester at the palace, and there have been many court balls to take up his mind.

MATENKO. If only I dared go to him and ask for the money! But I cannot! (*Drops his head on the table.*) Is there nothing in the house for supper?

ELZUNIA. Nothing, my husband. We ate the last slice of bread for breakfast. Even the hens have stopped laying. There is not so much as one egg. Just this old dried onion is left. (*She tosses the onion to him. He takes it and fingers it as she talks.*) Let us go to bed and forget our hunger.

(*She rises, but he jumps up and goes after her.*)

MATENKO. Wait! I have an idea! Things will get no better. You must go to the Queen and tell her I have died. First rub your eyes with this onion. If we cannot eat it, let it bring us some food.

ELZUNIA. But suppose she should discover you are living?

MATENKO. She has never come this way. And perhaps she will give you the money for a decent burial that she has not given us for these last years on earth.

ELZUNIA. Very well, then. I will do it.

(*They rub her eyes with the onion, and she takes a hand-kerchief from her pocket.*)

MATENKO. A little more, wife. Let us make them red and swollen, as if you had been crying all the night.

ELZUNIA. (*Pretending great grief.*) There! Am I wretched enough to go to the palace?

MATENKO. (*Rubbing his hands in delight.*) Yes, yes! This is my very best trick—if it works! Now go at once!

ELZUNIA. I shall be back as soon as possible, my husband. Wish me luck in my sorrow!

(She runs out the door, laughing, old MATENKO *watching her. The* CURTAINS *close.)*

SCENE THREE

ANNOUNCER.   An hour passes, and Elzunia is running down the road to the cottage. Matenko is waiting for her at the open door.

(The ANNOUNCER *leaves and the* CURTAINS *open, to reveal* ELZUNIA, *running up to the cottage door.)*

MATENKO.   What luck, wife?   What luck?

ELZUNIA.   It was easy!   It's too bad you can't die every day. Look!   Fifty gold pieces to give their old jester a decent burial!

MATENKO.   Did you see the King?

ELZUNIA.   No.   I found the Queen alone in the garden.   I sobbed out my story, and she felt so badly she gave me all the money she had in her little blue purse.   She said this would be enough to bury you, and still leave me money to live on!

MATENKO.   *(Grabbing her around the waist and twirling her.)*   Wife, it's a wonderful trick!   And now it's your turn to die!   I shall go to the King and tell him you have left me alone and desolate.

ELZUNIA.   But suppose he should find out the truth?

MATENKO.   That difficulty we shall have to solve if the time comes.   Meanwhile, I must try my luck with King Jan. Where is the onion?   *(She gets it, and they rub it on his face.)*   Ouch! . . . There!   *(As she puts the onion down on the table.)*   Now I am ready to go and tell him that my dear wife is dead, and I am alone in the world and penniless. *(He is the picture of misery as he leaves the house. He sobs, and his shoulders shake.)*   Where is the basket?   If the King gives me gold, I shall stop at the market for food.

ELZUNIA. (*Calls after him.*) Good-by, old man. Good luck! (*Sighs.*) Well, it will not hurry him to wait by the open door. Now that we have gold pieces, we shall have dinner. I may as well put the plates and cups on the table.

(*She bustles about the room, getting dishes from the cupboard and setting the table. There is a* RAP *at the door; she goes and finds a* BEGGAR *standing outside it.*)

Yes, old fellow?

BEGGAR. (*Slyly.*) Could you give an old man a crust of bread?

ELZUNIA. Alas, sir, we haven't a bite of bread in the house.

BEGGAR. But you are setting the table with plates and bowls.

ELZUNIA. I am waiting for my husband to come home from the palace. He has gone to get food.

BEGGAR. (*With a sneer.*) He will get no food at the palace, my good woman. Many a time I have waited by their kitchen door. But perhaps you have gold pieces in some crock or pot? (*Sidles into the room.*) Some you can spare?

ELZUNIA. What would a poor woman without so much as a loaf of bread be doing with gold pieces?

BEGGAR. (*Peering here and there.*) You wouldn't mind if I looked about?

ELZUNIA. (*Angrily.*) Yes, I would mind. If you will come again when my husband gets back, there will be plenty to eat!

BEGGAR. (*Snatches up the dried onion from the table.*) What is this?

ELZUNIA. That? Why, that's just an old dried onion—one that's brought us good luck.

BEGGAR. Good luck, eh? Then I'll take it along for myself. Does it put gold in your pockets?

ELZUNIA. (*Beginning to twinkle.*) It has.

BEGGAR. Then I'll take the onion and go. Never mind the supper, old woman. I'll see what good luck this will bring.

At least I can put it between two slices of bread. Some good wife will see to that!

(*He puts it in his pocket, and skips out.*)

ELZUNIA. (*Laughing heartily as he goes.*) Too bad, old dried-up onion! But you have served us well. One bag of gold already—and if you have kept a thief from the cupboard, I guess we can let you go. Who knows? Perhaps it is best to get rid of you now! You were our very best trick! What will Matenko say when I tell him I gave you away? (*Looks out the door again.*) But here he comes now! Down the road as fast as his legs will carry him. What luck, Matenko? What luck?

MATENKO. (*Entering with a heavy bag and a basket of food.*) My dear wife, the King's sympathy is worth even more than the Queen's! Two hundred gold pieces! Enough to bury you. Enough to stop my grief. And enough to keep us the rest of our lives.

(*Puts the bag on the table.*)

ELZUNIA. Let us count it out now. Here, Matenko, you take that pile; I'll take this.

MATENKO. Very well.

(*They begin to count.*)

ELZUNIA. Ten, twenty, thirty, forty, fifty . . . and a hundred gold pieces! What a wonderful trick! (*Laughs heartily.*) But suppose the King should tell the Queen?

MATENKO. Sixty, seventy, eighty, ninety—one—two—three —four gold pieces! And here, wife, in the basket, is food. More food than has been in our kitchen for a long time. Bread, meat, butter, milk, flour. So you can bake a cake for the funeral feast! I bought it on my way home from the palace.

ELZUNIA. Well, let us have some bread at once. (*She cuts off two slices, and they sit down to eat.*) Tonight we shall have a banquet. I shall make soup, roast the meat, bake the cake, and— Why, what is it, husband?

MATENKO. (*He has been looking out the window, and is*

suddenly the picture of distress.) Wife! (*His mouthful of bread chokes him, and he can hardly get the words out.*) Wife, look! The King and Queen are coming! Far up the road I can see them!

ELZUNIA. (*Runs to look where he is pointing.*) Are you sure?

MATENKO. Of course; their gold crowns are bright in the sunshine. Come, we had better lie down on the floor and pretend we are really dead, in case they come here!

ELZUNIA. Let us put a coating of flour on our faces and place a candle at our heads and one at our feet!
  (*Both smear flour on each other with much giggling. ELZUNIA lights the candles.*)

MATENKO. Hurry, wife! They are almost to the cottage!

ELZUNIA. Well, lie down then. I am ready.
  (*He lies down, and she does likewise.*)

MATENKO. Stop laughing, Elzunia! They will never believe we are dead!

ELZUNIA. You stop! Whenever you giggle, I have to!
  (*Then both lie very still, as the KING and QUEEN come to the open door.*)

KING. Now we shall see which of them is dead.

QUEEN. (*Arguing.*) I *know* it was Matenko, my dear.

KING. But didn't I say that Matenko himself came to me not half an hour ago? I say it was Elzunia!

QUEEN. Look! Here they are—both of them—dead!

KING. Together on the floor. Then each of us is right. Poor old souls. I'm afraid I have neglected them these last few months.

QUEEN. I wonder what it was that took them?

KING. He was the best jester that ever played a joke in our court. It's too bad his poor wits failed him.
  (*Wipes his eyes.*)

QUEEN. We have never had a cook with the skill of Elzunia. Poor woman! (*Wipes her eyes.*) Well, my lord, there is nothing we can do now but bury them. Let us go and take care of it.

KING. Very well. I do wonder, though, which of the two old folks died first.

MATENKO. (*Rising up suddenly.*) Your Majesty, though my wife died first, I assure you, I was dead before!

KING. (*Greatly startled. Then he laughs.*) You rascal! Get up immediately and tell us what this trickery means!

MATENKO. (*He and* ELZUNIA *both rise shamefacedly.*) We were penniless, Your Majesty; for the money that you promised never came.

ELZUNIA. And no one would give work to two such old people. There was nothing in the house to eat. Just one old dried-up onion.

MATENKO. So I thought of this trick, and it worked so well when Elzunia tried it, that I played it, too!

KING. (*Thoughtfully.*) I see, my old friend. It is really I who am to blame. And for that I shall give you two hundred more gold pieces—enough to keep you both as long as you live. But I leave it on one condition—that you promise never to use your wits dishonestly again!

ELZUNIA. I promise, my lord. In fact, I have given the onion away.

MATENKO. (*Solemnly.*) And I promise, my lord. I do indeed. The next time I die, you will know that I am really dead!

(*All laugh, and the* CURTAINS *close.*)

Production Notes

PROPERTIES:

cane for the jester
onion
handkerchief
2 bags of gold pieces
basket filled with bread, vegetables,
   food, etc.
bag of flour
2 plates, 2 cups, 2 knives and
   spoons
pots and crocks in cupboard
2 thrones
2 benches
table
cupboard
2 small chairs or stools

COSTUMES:

KING JAN wears a knee-length tunic, brilliantly colored and richly ornamented. In addition to this, he wears a long cape and crown, long hose, and bright slippers.

The QUEEN and her LADIES wear long, ornate gowns, belted at the waist, with rather full skirts. Jewels are at the neck or on the collar, and in the headbands.

MATENKO wears the traditional jester's outfit of jerkin with tights of brilliant colors, in the first scene. In the last two scenes, he wears a peasant's tunic and knee-length trousers and boots.

ELZUNIA is dressed in a wide full skirt of bright material, peasant blouse, bodice, and babushka.

The MEN OF THE COURT are arrayed like the king, but less elaborately and without crowns.

The BEGGAR appears in very ragged peasant's clothing.

THE CROWNING OF ARTHUR

A British Legend

THE LEGENDS of King Arthur are among those best-loved and most frequently dramatized by both boys and girls. Of them, a favorite is the story of how Arthur drew the sword from the anvil, and his subsequent coronation. It combines the courage, chivalry, and supernatural of the medieval period. Because of these qualities, it has been selected to represent Great Britain, although there are hundreds of other folk tales and legends which are as authentic, if not as representative, of the country. In this dramatization, two of the Arthurian legends are combined to unify and complete the story.

CHARACTERS

ARTHUR, *a young squire*
SIR ECTOR, *his father*
SIR KAY, *elder son of Ector*
THE ARCHBISHOP
SIR BAUDWIN OF WALES
SIR ULFIUS OF CORNWALL
SIR BRASTIUS OF THE MARSHES
A STOUT YEOMAN
MERLIN, *the wise man*
KNIGHTS and LADIES, *any number*
COMMON PEOPLE, *any number*
NARRATOR

SCENE ONE: *The road to the tournament fields.*

SCENE TWO: *The churchyard; one hour later.*

SCENE THREE: *The churchyard; three months later.*

THE CROWNING OF ARTHUR

THE SCENE is a road leading to the tournament fields in London. There may be trees, bushes, and rocks, suggesting the country, to the R., from which direction SIR ECTOR *and his sons approach. To the L. is a brightly colored tent with pennants, indicating that this is the edge of the field, their destination. If the play is done more simply, there need be nothing at all in the way of scenery, except perhaps a log or rock to sit on; for it is used only as atmosphere, and is not essential to the business.*

❖　　❖　　❖　　❖

NARRATOR. There was once in Britain a wise and pious knight named Sir Ector. He, with his two sons, Kay and Arthur, lived peaceably in their mountain castle, many miles from London Town. Both sons were trained to a noble manhood; and in due time, Kay, the elder, was knighted, while Arthur became a squire. It was the dearest wish of the two boys to attend a tournament; so when one was held on the New Year's Day following Kay's knighting, Sir Ector granted them permission to go; and the three set out for London. It is on the road near the tournament field where the first scene takes place. Many knights and ladies have already gathered, as Sir Ector and his sons approach. They have left their horses at the inn where they stayed the night, and so are coming the rest of the way on foot.

(*As the* CURTAINS *open, the three walk in from D.R.,* SIR ECTOR *leading the way. The* BOYS *are excited and eager to reach the tournament.* SIR ECTOR *stops to speak.*)

ECTOR. Yonder is the tournament field. (*Points off L.*) Already many have come, though the jousts do not begin until tomorrow.

KAY. And that, Father—that tent with the flags flying from the top—what is that?

ECTOR. That is a pavilion, my Son, set up for the contests.

57

ARTHUR. Look, Father, in the distance are many more of them! All colors! With flags on the top of each!

ECTOR. Oh, yes. The fields are large, and we have just come to the edge of them. There is a tent for each castle. We shall see many more by night.

KAY. The horses, Father! Never have I seen so many! And such beautiful ones! (*In dismay.*) Should we not have ridden in to the grounds?

ECTOR. It is better that we left our horses at the inn, my Son. They have brought us a long distance, and will not be fresh for the tournament if we use them today.

KAY. (*Pouting.*) But people will think we are poor knights who have no horses if we come on foot.

ECTOR. (*Rather sternly.*) Does it matter what they think? Our horses need refreshment as we ourselves did last night. We have come farther than most of these knights, and we have but one horse each. If they are to be fresh tomorrow, they must have rest. Remember, my Son, that we have come here not to impress others with our wealth, but to try our skills.

KAY. (*Humbly.*) Yes, Father.

ECTOR. There is much we can see on foot. Tonight we shall return to the inn, and tomorrow morning set out with horses that are fresh.

ARTHUR. There are many who are walking. Look, Brother, over yonder by the tent! And the crowds in the distance! (*Turning to his father, who has just sat down on a rock near by.*) I did not know there were so many people in all London Town!

ECTOR. (*Laughing.*) There are many more than you see here, Arthur. Here we shall see only the Knights and Ladies, and there are many poor and common folk in London.

ARTHUR. (*His eyes shining.*) But is this not the most splendid tournament there has ever been? Surely every knight in the realm is here.

ECTOR. (*Laughing again.*) No, my boy. It is a sight to you who have never seen another. But this is small compared to the tournaments of the King. When Uther ruled, they were held at the castle; and for weeks at a time, feasting, reveling, and jousting went on!

KAY. For weeks, Father?

ECTOR. Aye, my Son. Uther was more fond of valiant deeds than anything in the world. And to his death, tournaments were held each year for all the knights in the kingdom to take part. (*Sighs.*) Would he had left an heir. Though the end of his reign was evil, it was not so bad as this lawlessness that's come after.

KAY. But must Britain be forever without a king? Is there no successor?

ECTOR. I do not know, my boy. Strange things go on at court, and we who are so far away know little about them. But for fifteen years no one has been found to succeed him. Perhaps this year. Who knows? We shall pray for the coming of a wise and just ruler.

KAY. Yes, Father. But now let us go in to the field. I am impatient to see what is beyond.

ECTOR. (*Rising from his seat.*) Very well, my boy. Let us go.
(*They start across to stage L., when* KAY *suddenly realizes that he does not have his sword.*)

KAY. Father! Arthur! I do not have my sword! I must have left it behind at the inn. This is only an empty scabbard!

ECTOR. You will not need it today, my boy. Get it tonight.

KAY. But I cannot walk about without a sword! Who will know I am a knight? They will take me for your squire!

ECTOR. (*With a smile.*) Which you were until a month ago.

KAY. (*Despairing.*) Oh, Father, what can I do?

ARTHUR. (*After a pause, quietly.*) I will go back after it,

Brother. It will not take me long; and since I am a squire, it is my place to fetch it.

KAY. You are the best squire in all Britain, Arthur!

ARTHUR. You go on in. I will get the sword and bring it to you here.

ECTOR. You can find your way back, Son?

ARTHUR. Of course. I will run and get it in no time at all. Farewell!

(ARTHUR *runs off D.R. quickly. At this moment, a* KNIGHT *enters from L. and recognizes* SIR ECTOR. *It is* SIR BAUDWIN. *He speaks as* ECTOR *and* KAY *reach the D.L. end of the stage.*)

BAUDWIN. Sir Ector! Is it my old friend, Ector?

ECTOR. Sir Baudwin! I am glad to see you! It is a long time since we have met.

BAUDWIN. Not since the last tournament of Uther. You were not much older than this lad here.

ECTOR. This is my son, Kay, Sir Baudwin.

KAY. How do you do, sir?

BAUDWIN. And you are a knight, eh, boy?

KAY. (*Proudly.*) Yes, sir. (*After a moment; eagerly.*) And this is my first tournament!

BAUDWIN. Your father's name is something to live up to. Fifteen years ago there was no knight in the Kingdom who rode as well as he.

KAY. (*Astonished.*) As you, Father? You have not told us.

ECTOR. Sir Baudwin flatters me. (*Turning back to Baudwin.*) But my tournament days are over, with the passing of Uther.

BAUDWIN. Ah, so? (*Shakes his head sadly.*) Well, I can't say that I blame you. A man is better off in his own castle in these lawless times. But now and again—

ECTOR. And has no heir been discovered? No kin?

BAUDWIN. There have been those who made claims, but no

rightful heir. Of that, I am certain. A strange thing has come about, though. For some weeks now there has been, in the churchyard yonder, a sword sticking in an anvil.

KAY. I saw it, Father, as we passed.

BAUDWIN. It appeared suddenly one morning, and the Archbishop has had five knights guarding it since. The inscription reads that whoever can pull it out is born king of the Britons.

ECTOR. Have any tried?

BAUDWIN. Oh, many. But no one can budge it.

ECTOR. (*Sadly.*) So Britain is without a king, and none can be found. It is sad, indeed.

BAUDWIN. But, come, I am taking your time, standing here talking. Are you on your way to the grounds?

ECTOR. Yes. My younger son, Arthur, has gone back to the inn; but he will join us when he returns. Shall we go in together?

BAUDWIN. By all means. Let us go.

(*The three pass on out D.L. After a moment, two more knights,* SIR ULFIUS *and* SIR BRASTIUS, *enter from R.*)

ULFIUS. (*As they cross.*) This must be the road. They said at the inn it was not far.

BRASTIUS. No, or so many would not have left their horses behind.

ULFIUS. Look! Already the flags and pavilions appear!

BRASTIUS. Let us hurry. We shall find our comrades here before us.

(*They hurry off L. in the direction the others have gone. After a moment,* ARTHUR *appears from R., carrying in his hand a beautiful sword. He stops for a moment, looks about him, and speaks to himself.*)

ARTHUR. This is the spot where I left them. But I am back so soon they cannot have gone far. (*As* KAY *appears L.*) Brother Kay!

KAY. How is it you are here already? Have you not gone to the inn at all?

ARTHUR. I did not have to, Brother. For as I was passing the churchyard yonder, I saw a sword—much better than yours—sticking in an anvil.

KAY. In an anvil? . . . Yes, Arthur, go on!

ARTHUR. There was no one around; so I pulled it out. It cannot belong to anyone, I am sure. Here, will it do?
(*He hands the sword to* KAY.)

KAY. (*Astonished and excited.*) Will it do? Indeed, it is better than mine. Say nothing to our father of this. But, come, he has met friends just inside. Let us find him at once.
(*The two hurry off D.L. and the* CURTAINS *close on the first scene.*)

SCENE TWO

THIS SCENE takes place in the churchyard. Just R. of C. there is a huge marble block with an anvil on it. Upstage, L. of C., is the church door. Nothing else is needed on the stage.

◇　　◇　　◇　　◇

NARRATOR. Scene Two is the churchyard. It is less than an hour later. The boys have shown their father the sword, and he has taken them at once to the place where it was found.
(*The* NARRATOR *leaves the stage, the* CURTAINS *open, and the* THREE *hurry in from off L.*)

ECTOR. It was here you say you found it, Kay?

KAY. Yes, Father.

ECTOR. You pulled it from the anvil by yourself?

KAY. (*After a moment's hesitation.*) Yes, Father. There was no one else near.

ECTOR. It has been well-guarded. I wonder that no one is

here now. But perhaps they have gone to the jousts. Take it, Son; if you have pulled it out, you must be able to drive it back in.

KAY. (*In horror.*) Oh, no, Father! I cannot!

ECTOR. Try it, Son.

KAY. (*Tries, but fails miserably.*) I cannot, Father.

ECTOR. (*Suspiciously.*) Are you sure that it was you who drew it forth?

KAY. (*After a moment.*) No, Father, it was not I.

ECTOR. Who was it, then?

KAY. (*Truthfully.*) It was Arthur.

ECTOR. Arthur? (*Turning to* ARTHUR, *and speaking almost sharply.*) Was it you, boy? Speak up!

ARTHUR. (*Simply.*) Yes, Father, I pulled it out. And I can put it back again.

(*He replaces the sword easily, and stands by the marble block.*)

ECTOR. (*Hardly believing his eyes.*) Yes, yes, I see. Now, can you draw it forth a second time?

(ARTHUR *takes it from the anvil as easily as he has put it in. He waits again for his father to speak.*)

Then it is true? My Son, do you know what this means?

ARTHUR. (*Bewildered.*) No, Father, I do not.

ECTOR. Read the inscription—along the blade.

ARTHUR. (*Reading with difficulty, and not comprehending.*) "Whoever pulls this sword from the anvil is rightly born king of the Britons." (*Puzzled.*) I do not understand. What does it mean?

ECTOR. (*After a moment.*) That you are heir to the throne of King Uther. That you are no longer my son.

ARTHUR. Oh, no, Father! That cannot be!

ECTOR. It is true. I am not your father, nor is Kay your brother. For I must tell you now that you were found many years ago in the forest. And your birth is unknown to me.

ARTHUR. *(Thrusting the sword back into the anvil.)* No!
I would rather be your son and squire than be king of the
Britons!

ECTOR. No, my boy. What heaven has decreed must come
to pass. It is not for us to decide. We must find the Archbishop at once. Come, he may be in the church.

(SIR ECTOR, *followed by the unwilling* ARTHUR *and the
abashed* SIR KAY, *go to the door of the church. The* CUR-
TAINS *close.*)

SCENE THREE

NARRATOR. It is Easter time. Knights from all over Britain
have gathered in the churchyard in answer to the Archbishop's summons. The story of Arthur's feat has astonished
some and angered others, but he is finally called to see if
he can accomplish the feat again—and so prove himself heir
to the throne.

(*The* NARRATOR *leaves the stage, and the* CURTAINS *part
to show the same scene as the previous one, except that
now there are many* KNIGHTS *and* LADIES *about, talking
noisily together. The* ARCHBISHOP *himself stands L. of
the marble block.* SIR ECTOR, SIR KAY, *and* ARTHUR *stand
beside him.*)

ARCHBISHOP. Peace, peace! (*The group becomes quiet at
the sound of his voice.*) As you have all heard, there is one
who has drawn forth the sword placed here by the hand of
God. There is but one meaning to this—that the boy,
Arthur, is chosen for our King.

(*There is an angry murmur from the crowd. The* ARCH-
BISHOP *stops it as he continues.*)

Yet there are some in this realm who will not consent without proof. And so I offer to all who desire it, a chance to
make further trial. And I pray that God will show clearly
which of us he has chosen. Now, who will be first?

(*There is a moment of hesitation, then the elderly* SIR
BAUDWIN *steps forward.*)

BAUDWIN. I will try, Father.

ARCHBISHOP. Very well. (*Announcing in a loud voice.*)
Sir Baudwin of Wales!
   (BAUDWIN *grasps the sword, and attempts to pull it out,
   but he cannot.*)

BAUDWIN. (*Good-naturedly.*) It is plain that I am not heir
to the throne.
   (*All laugh as he moves away from the marble block.*)

ARCHBISHOP. Who will be next?

ULFIUS. (*Arrogantly.*) I will, Father, if I may.

ARCHBISHOP. Sir Ulfius of Cornwall! Go ahead, my son.
   (ULFIUS *tries and tries; but he, too, is unable to move it.
   Finally he steps back angrily.*)

ULFIUS. It is all a trick! No one could move it!
   (*Again the people laugh as he moves away.*)

ARCHBISHOP. And is there another who would try?

BRASTIUS. (*After a moment of hesitation.*) I will, Father.

ARCHBISHOP. Sir Brastius of the Marshes! Take your turn.
   (BRASTIUS *tries again and again; but however hard he
   struggles, the sword will not move.*)

ARCHBISHOP. It is not a matter of strength or skill. To the
chosen one, the Lord will give the power.

BRASTIUS. (*Angrily.*) I do not believe there is any man
who can budge it!

ARCHBISHOP. Will anyone else try? (*There is a pause, then
a stout* YEOMAN *steps up.*) Yes, my lad?

YEOMAN. I would like to try, Father. I am of humble birth;
but if such as they have failed, perhaps the skill is not to be
found in the nobly born.

ARCHBISHOP. You are welcome, indeed. Try your hand.
   (*The* YEOMAN *tries; but he, like the others, cannot do it.*)
Is there yet another? (*No one replies.*) No? Very well,

65

then, my boy, will you see if you can do it again? (*He has turned to* ARTHUR, *and now announces in a loud voice:*) Arthur, son of Sir Ector of Lyonesse!

(ARTHUR *grasps the sword, and draws it easily from the anvil. There is a murmur of surprise in the crowd.*)

BRASTIUS. This is no miracle! It is a trick. We do not want to be ruled by a boy!

ULFIUS. See if he can put it back again! That is the test!

ARCHBISHOP. Very well, Sir Ulfius. Arthur, see if you can replace it.

(ARTHUR *does so with ease, and the crowd murmurs again.*)

BRASTIUS. Now that it is loosened, any man can draw it! Let me try!

ARCHBISHOP. Certainly, Sir Brastius, go ahead.

(BRASTIUS *tries, but cannot remove the sword now, any more than he could the first time. Angrily he gives up, and walks D.R. amid jeers and laughter of the crowd.*) Arthur, as a final test, once more draw it forth. (*Again* ARTHUR *removes the sword, and the* CROWD *is talking excitedly now.*) Peace! (*They quiet down to listen.*) Clearly there is one whom the Lord has set apart. All who have wished have tried, and all who have tried have failed— all but Arthur. For fifteen years we have been without a king. Things have gone from bad to worse in the realm. Yet no heir was found. Now one has been sent—

BRASTIUS. How do we know this is not a trick of Sir Ector? To make his son king?

(*The* CROWD *takes up this argument, calling ad lib remarks, such as "Yes, yes! How do we know?" etc.*)

ECTOR. (*Coming forward with dignity.*) It is not a trick, though of his birth I know as little as you yourselves.

ULFIUS. What do you mean?

ECTOR. (*Simply.*) That I found him, a tiny babe, in the forest many years ago. There was no one near and nothing to show who he might be, except a tiny gold chain about his neck. On it were engraved the words, "His name shall be Arthur." I took him home with me, and for fifteen years he has been as my own son.

BRASTIUS. Indeed, that is a fine story! But we want no boy for our king!

ULFIUS. (*Angrily.*) He and the Archbishop have plotted together! Found in the forest! . . . A likely tale!

(*The* CROWD *begins to shout, some taking the side of* BRASTIUS *and* ULFIUS, *and some taking the side of* ECTOR. *Ad lib remarks such as, "Yes, a likely tale! Hail, Arthur! Hail to our king! No, he is not our king!" fill the air. The shouting grows, neither side giving in, when suddenly out of the church door comes an old man—*MERLIN. *He speaks in a clear voice which miraculously stops their clamoring.*)

MERLIN. Do you ask further proof of his royal birth?

(*Many in the* CROWD *shout, "Yes, yes!"*)

Behold then, I will tell you. I am called Merlin—or Merlin the Wizard. I was with old King Uther when he died in his castle by the sea. As I stood looking out across the waves, a babe was carried to me on the water, and left by the rocks at my feet. From the signs I had read in the heavens, I knew that this child was heir to the throne, and would someday be king of the Britons. I took him, as I was bade, to the mountain side; and there I left him. But I knew he should be found and well cared for until such time as it pleased heaven to crown him. His name was on the locket. Hail to Arthur, King of Britain!

(*All are now convinced, and join heartily to the calls of confidence, "Hail to Arthur! Crown him at once!" They kneel before him; and* ARTHUR, *too, kneels as the* ARCHBISHOP *lifts the sword to knight him. He gives* ARTHUR *the knighthood with three gentle strokes.*)

ARCHBISHOP. Sir Arthur, be to the world the image of courage, truth, and gentility. Let men in all ages admire the honor that is yours. (*Then he places the crown on* ARTHUR'S *head.*)   Arise, and be King of the Britons for as long as you shall live!

(*Everyone calls, "Hail, hail to King Arthur! Hail!" etc. And so, amid great shouting and joy, the* CURTAINS *close.*)

Production Notes

PROPERTIES:

swords for all knights
shields for some of them
crown
anvil on a large block
door to the church
rocks, bushes, end of tent (if desired)

COSTUMES:

WARRIOR OF
KING ARTHUR

All the KNIGHTS wore knee-length tunics with normal belted waist. If possible, these should suggest a shirt of mail. Aluminum or silver-bronze paint on a coarse fabric will give the illusion Long hose, soft shoes, and hoods completed this costume, although smooth bobs were worn in the early medieval period, and are much easier to simulate.

LADIES wore their hair long and flowing, or parted in the middle, with braids. Gowns were simple in style. Unbelted and fitting the body rather closely, they had long flowing skirts and long tight sleeves. A mantle, or circular cape, was fastened at the throat. The luxurious materials were in bright, gem-like colors, with strong contrasts of dark and light. Many garments were parti-colored, and heraldic designs were popular. The effects were rich and brilliant.

The ARCHBISHOP wears a white cassock or simple, long tunic with black hooded overgarment. On his head is an ornate mitre; and in his hand, a crozier. The crozier in this period assumed the crook shape and stood higher than a human figure. Crosses, squares, and circles were used over and over again in embroidery design.

MERLIN wears a black or dark robe with long loose sleeves and a high neck. It is long and belted loosely at the waist. He wears a Dante cap and a long flowing beard.

SHIELDS are round in shape with rich ornamentation. They may be constructed of corrugated paper, and either painted with aluminum paint or covered with silver paper. A strip of muslin fastened across the back will make them practical in scenes where they are carried.

ANVIL AND MARBLE BLOCK:

The block can best be simulated by a large wooden box painted to resemble marble. If the anvil were constructed of papier-mâché, it would probably be most effective. Good results, however, might be obtained by building up an armature of wood and wrapping it with strips of cloth or newspapers, gluing it together securely, and painting it black. If a large quantity of glue is mixed with the paint, it will be less likely to soak into the material, and it will make a harder, stiffer-appearing surface. A place to stick the sword, on the side away from the audience, must be provided for the smooth working of the business involved.

TRAVELERS FROM OLYMPUS

A Greek Legend

A MIRACLE of ancient times is the theme of the familiar old story of Philemon and Baucis. The elderly couple are grieved at the cruel ways of their neighbors, and give shelter to every stranger who passes by, rather than to allow him to become a victim of the evil townsfolk. How they unknowingly take in two gods who are disguised as human beings is a delightful and touching legend. No matter how much food is eaten, even more remains, and the mystery culminates in the total destruction of the city, with only the two old people left to survive. A temple springs up overnight. They are made the custodians, and are to be hosts to all who pass by for as long as they both shall live.

CHARACTERS

PHILEMON, *an elderly man of Greece*

BAUCIS, *his wife*

JUPITER, *god of the heavens*

MERCURY, *messenger of the gods and
    patron of travelers*

THE STORY TELLER

FIRST VILLAGER

SECOND VILLAGER

THIRD VILLAGER

FOURTH VILLAGER

SCENE 1.   *The cottage of Philemon and Baucis, in ancient
Greece; evening.*

SCENE 2.   *The same; the next morning.*

TRAVELERS FROM OLYMPUS

SCENE ONE

THE REQUIREMENTS are the same for both scenes of this play: hearth and stool D.R.; cupboard U.C.; chair U.L.; table, with a chair at R. and L. of it, D.L.C.; a chest against wall D.L. Doors are U.R. and L., respectively. The room is small, obviously the main room in the house, and used for eating as well as working and sitting by the fire. A pitcher of milk and several crockery dishes are on the rough table.

❖   ❖   ❖   ❖

STORY TELLER.   Once upon a time in Ancient Greece there was a city in which the people had grown wicked and selfish. Whenever strangers entered the gates, the townsfolk closed their cottage doors; and some even hit the strangers with sticks and stones. Instead of making wanderers or new neighbors feel welcome, they would drive them away with hard words. On the outskirts of this town lived an old couple in a tiny cottage thatched with straw. Though they were very poor, they were happy together, and always welcomed any stranger who came to their gate. There are two scenes in our play. The first takes place in the cottage one evening. The characters are Philemon, the old man; Baucis, his wife; Jupiter and Mercury, the two gods; and several men and women of the city.

(*The* STORY TELLER *leaves, and the* CURTAINS *open, showing* PHILEMON *as he sits before the fire; and* BAUCIS, *who is standing before the cupboard.*)

PHILEMON.   Do come and rest by the fire, my good wife. It is early, and the supper will wait.

BAUCIS.   (*Coming closer.*)   The meal is a simple one, Philemon, not worth waiting for long.

PHILEMON.   The food is good, and what matter if the fare is light?   It is enough for a man after a long day's work.

BAUCIS. (*Sitting.*)   All of the vineyards in Greece seem to be yielding their grapes at once. You have been at our neighbor's since early morning, and it is already beginning to grow dark.

PHILEMON.   True, wife. And they are not all gathered in yet.

BAUCIS.   He will want you for the wines, I suppose?

PHILEMON.   (*Smiling at her.*) Of what good is a vine-dresser if he doesn't stay through the harvest?

BAUCIS.   No, husband, I did not mean that. But our own grapes are ripening, and there is no one to pick them. What you earn at our neighbor's you will lose here at home!

PHILEMON.   Tonight perhaps I can work for a while in our garden. Not only the grapes are ripening. Other fruit as well.

BAUCIS.   Do not worry, husband. The gods have been good to us. We have our cottage, our vineyards, and each other. We are poor, but our life has been a happy one.

PHILEMON.   Happier than our neighbor's, I dare say. With all his wealth he has not learned the secret—that giving is greater than getting, and that kindness brings more satisfaction than cruelty.

BAUCIS.   It is true. (*Sighs sadly. There is a pause, then* BAUCIS *speaks again.*) Shall I put another stick on the fire?

PHILEMON.   Our woodpile is getting low. Perhaps we should save it until I have time to chop more.

BAUCIS.   As you say. But the evenings are chilly.

(*There is a* COMMOTION *outside,* CRIES *and* FOOTSTEPS.)

PHILEMON.   (*Starting in his chair.*) Hark! What is that?

BAUCIS.   (*Listening a moment.*) Cries of people in the street!

PHILEMON.   As if they were hooting someone through the village! Some beggar . . .

BAUCIS.   Let us go and look!

(*Rises and goes to the door U.R.*)

PHILEMON.   (*Rises and follows her.*) Time was when a

74

stranger could get a night's lodging in this town!   Now he is driven from the city gates like a stray dog.   Look!

BAUCIS.   Here they come!   Two men!

PHILEMON.   Both well-dressed!   And our neighbor leads the mob!

BAUCIS.   Let us ask them in, husband.   We have little to offer, but it's better than being stoned through the streets.

PHILEMON.   (*Stepping to the doorstep.*)   Hello there, strangers!   Friends!

BAUCIS.   Come to our doorstep!

PHILEMON.   We mean no harm!   You are welcome!

(*The* VILLAGERS *are* MUTTERING *together, and some speak out as they come to the door of the cottage.*)

FIRST VILLAGER.   What are you mixing in this for?

SECOND VILLAGER.   It's none of your business!

THIRD VILLAGER.   They may be thieves!

FOURTH VILLAGER.   How do you know they don't plan to steal our gold and murder us in our sleep?

FIRST VILLAGER.   Better go back in your cottage, old man!

SECOND VILLAGER.   Yes, and the old woman, too!

PHILEMON.   Peace, peace!   I am not afraid of these travelers. Let them pass.

BAUCIS.   We have nothing worth stealing.   But if they are hungry, we can give them bread!

THIRD VILLAGER.   (*Laughing.*)   You pair of old fools! Hardly enough for yourselves, and you want to feed all the tramps who come through the town.

FOURTH VILLAGER.   Last week it was a stray dog—and they gave it their supper!

(*All the mob laugh loudly at this.*)

PHILEMON.   (*With dignity.*)   That is our affair.   I beg you, let the travelers in, if they would enter.

BAUCIS.   Please do, sirs.   Our cottage is humble and our supper light. But if you will share it with us, we shall be honored.

JUPITER. (*Who is the older of the two strangers.*) Gladly, my good woman. (*To his companion.*) Let us go in.

MERCURY. Yes. Peace! Let us by.

FIRST VILLAGER. (*In a surly tone.*) Very well, then.

SECOND VILLAGER. You'll not get any thanks for your kindness, old man!

FOURTH VILLAGER. No, nor money for your pains!

THIRD VILLAGER. It's his affair. Come along.

FOURTH VILLAGER. Yes, let them find out for themselves. It's nothing out of our pockets!

(*The other* VILLAGERS *laugh derisively, turn and go, their* VOICES DYING AWAY *in the distance.* PHILEMON *closes the cottage door when the others have entered.*)

PHILEMON. I am ashamed for our city. They seem to have forgotten the meaning of kindness.

BAUCIS. But make yourselves at home. If you will rest by the fire, I will finish getting the supper. Put on another log, Philemon.

PHILEMON. (*Putting two good-sized ones on the fire.*) You must be tired from your journey—cold, too, with the evening air.

JUPITER. (*Sitting by the fire.*) Thank you, my friend. We have come a long way.

PHILEMON. (*Pausing a moment in his work.*) From what town?

JUPITER. A town . . . far from this one.

MERCURY. (*Also sitting by the fire.*) We had hoped to spend the night here and then go on in the morning.

PHILEMON. I'm afraid there is no place you can get lodging. There was once—but now even the inns that took travelers serve only our own people.

MERCURY. And what becomes of outsiders?

PHILEMON. (*Sadly.*) They receive the same treatment you did, my friend.

JUPITER. Someday your city will learn a lesson. They cannot turn their backs on the outside world.

MERCURY. Such actions will not go forever unpunished.

PHILEMON. They do not know. They do not understand any more. It has been so long since they have shared either their homes or their hearts . . .

MERCURY. And yet your people have prospered?

PHILEMON. Yes, my lord. They have grown rich in these years.

BAUCIS. (*Coming over to them.*) The supper is ready, sirs. It is not much—only what we should have had for ourselves. But come and sit down.

(*They rise and go to the table, which is simply set with a pitcher of milk, grapes, bread, and honey in a crock.*)

PHILEMON. (*Standing at one end of the table.*) Sit here, my friend. (*Indicating* JUPITER.) And you, sir, on this side.

(*He indicates* MERCURY. *Both gods sit.*)

BAUCIS. (*Passing the basket of grapes.*) These are grapes from our own vineyard.

PHILEMON. (*Passing the bread.*) Here is bread—and honey from our own bees.

MERCURY. (*Helping himself generously.*) How thick and rich it is! You are kind to us, friend.

JUPITER. There is nothing better than bread when one is hungry!

(*He, too, helps himself.*)

PHILEMON. And milk?

(*Offers* MERCURY *the pitcher.*)

MERCURY. (*Pours himself a cup.*) Thank you, my friend. (*Turns to his companion.*) Will you have some sweet milk?

JUPITER. Yes, indeed! (*Pours himself a generous cupful.*) Do you and your wife keep a cow?

PHILEMON. We had to sell her last winter. Since then, I have been getting milk and cheese from our neighbor. I work in his vineyards.

MERCURY. I see. He must give you the best. It's very good milk. (*Drinks it all down.*) May I have another cup?

BAUCIS. (*Apologetically.*) I'm afraid, sir, that is all we have——

PHILEMON. There was only one pitcher. Had we known you were coming——

MERCURY. But this one is full! There is plenty of milk! (*Pours himself another cup and drinks it.*)

JUPITER. I should like some more. (*Pours out another cup.*) And the honey, too. Won't you have a second cup? (*Handing the pitcher to* PHILEMON.)

PHILEMON. (*Amazed as he takes the pitcher and finds it as full as before.*) Well—why, yes, sir. I had not thought there was this much. Will you have some, wife?

BAUCIS. No, thank you. (*Looks at the pitcher and is as astonished as her husband.*) But—well, yes—a little. Let me get the other loaf of bread. (*She rises and goes to the hearth downstage.*)

JUPITER. Yes, I should like some more, my good woman, to eat with this honey.

BAUCIS. (*From the hearth.*) Philemon, Philemon! Will you come and slice this bread for me?

PHILEMON. (*Rising from his chair.*) Will you excuse me a moment? (*Both guests nod in assent, and continue to eat ravenously, as* PHILEMON *leaves the table and goes to his wife.*)

BAUCIS. (*In a low voice full of wonder.*) Have you noticed, husband, that the pitcher of milk is as full as ever, and we have each had two cups?

PHILEMON. (*In great wonder.*) Yes—and the honey jar has more in it now than when we sat down!

BAUCIS. Even the grapes which were small and sour are hanging in heavy clusters!

PHILEMON. They must be magicians! But come, wife, we must not be rude to our guests.

(*And they go back to the table with the bread, which* PHILEMON *has been cutting.*)

BAUCIS. (*Putting the plate of bread on the table.*) Here is the other loaf. You must have some of it.

MERCURY. Yes, indeed, and milk to drink with it.

(*He again helps himself most generously to both things.*)

JUPITER. Please forgive our great hunger. We have not dined since morning, and your supper is excellent.

PHILEMON. (*Whose eyes are by now nearly popping from his head.*) You are welcome. I—we—my wife and I had not thought there was enough food for guests——

JUPITER. There is plenty. I have never been so well filled.

BAUCIS. If you will stay overnight with us, there is a bed——

PHILEMON. We shall be happy to have you, my lords. You cannot go on your way in the dark.

BAUCIS. My husband and I can manage very well. The bed is not soft, but you are welcome to sleep in it.

MERCURY. Thank you. We should be pleased to stay.

JUPITER. But are we not taking your room?

PHILEMON. That is all right. We can manage out here.

BAUCIS. The hearth is warm. We have often slept here. You see, there is no other place for a guest.

JUPITER. Let us sleep by the fire.

PHILEMON. No, indeed. You must be rested to continue your journey.

MERCURY. (*Rising from the table.*) Then let us go into the bedroom now. I am tired, and if these good people are to sleep on the hearth, we must not keep them awake with our talking.

JUPITER. (*Rises also.*) Yes. We shall pay you well for your hospitality to strangers.

PHILEMON. Oh, no, sir. We are glad you will stay. I am only sorry we have not a finer place.

BAUCIS. And softer beds. But, come. I will show you the way.

(*She leads them out a door L., and the three disappear.*)

PHILEMON. (*Looking at the table.*) More of everything than when we sat down! Yet I have eaten well! I wonder who they can be? (*Sighing and looking up.*) I suppose it does not matter—only that we have taken them in.

(*He continues putting the dishes away, taking them from the table to the cupboard—when* BAUCIS *returns. She goes immediately to the table, and is as astonished as her husband.*)

BAUCIS. My husband, there is enough food for morning!

PHILEMON. Yes, it is as if we had not eaten at all!

BAUCIS. They must be noblemen. And yet——

PHILEMON. They did not say where they were from—or where they are going. Rich merchants, perhaps——

BAUCIS. Or magicians——

PHILEMON. It does not matter, wife. They were strangers who needed food and lodging, and we have been able to serve them.

(*Both the old people go on clearing the food away, as the* CURTAINS *close.*)

SCENE TWO

STORY TELLER. The second scene is early the next morning. The old couple slept well on the hard floor, and were up early to serve breakfast to their guests. Again, they put the food on the table; and again, no matter how heartily they ate, it did not disappear.

(*The* CURTAINS *open, and the stage is the same.* PHILE-
MON *and* BAUCIS *and the two* STRANGERS *are standing
in the center of the room.*)

PHILEMON. (*Addressing the travelers.*) It has been an
honor to have you stop with us, my lords.

BAUCIS. We wish you might stay longer.

PHILEMON. Perhaps you will come this way again—on your
return?

MERCURY. Your kindness to us will not be forgotten.

JUPITER. (*Walking to the door.*) Come, look from your
doorway!

PHILEMON. Yes, my lord. What——
(*He walks slowly to* JUPITER.)

BAUCIS. (*Frightened.*) What is it, sir?

JUPITER. Look upon your city!

BAUCIS. (*She, too, has gone to the doorway.*) But it—where
is it? Where the houses were——

PHILEMON. (*Rubbing his eyes.*) There is only a lake!
What—what has happened to it?

JUPITER. The two strangers whom you entertained so graciously are no less than gods. I am Jupiter, and my companion here, Mercury.

MERCURY. Your people had grown so wicked that we have
turned their city into a lake, and your neighbors into fish!

BAUCIS. But *that*, sir? That palace?

MERCURY. It is not a palace. It is a temple. A place of
beauty where before there was selfishness and sin.

JUPITER. (*With a smile.*) My good people, you alone have
been saved. And instead of a humble cottage, you shall have
a temple of the gods in which to welcome your guests. But
before we go, you may each ask a favor. Whatever your
wish, it will be granted.

PHILEMON. (*Without any hesitation.*) Let us, then, be the guardians of this temple as long as we live.

BAUCIS. And when it is time for us to go, let us die together, that neither may be left to mourn the other.

JUPITER. Your wishes shall be granted. And we thank you for your kindness to us.

MERCURY. (*Turning now to* PHILEMON.) By now you have guessed our destination—Olympus. Our work here is finished. Let us go.
(*Without a further word, both* GODS *step silently through the door and disappear from sight. The two* OLD PEOPLE *look after them for a moment, then* PHILEMON *speaks.*)

PHILEMON. Come, wife, let us go into the temple.

BAUCIS. And thank the gods for this miracle.
(*They go out joyfully, hand in hand. Before the* CURTAINS *close, the* STORY TELLER *returns to take up the final threads of the legend.*)

STORY TELLER. And so for many years the two old people looked after the temple. They entertained the strangers who passed by and they did it as gladly in the days of their good fortune as they had in their poverty. They did not forget the gods who had saved their lives and brought them to such a happy old age. Finally, one day as they were standing in front of the temple, a gentle wind swept over them, and they vanished. But in their stead, grew two majestic trees. Thus the two old people had both their wishes—to guard the temple and to die together. And so for many centuries the beautiful trees stood before the temple of Jupiter, and garlands were hung on their branches.

(STORY TELLER *leaves the stage, as the* CURTAINS *close.*)

Production Notes

PROPERTIES:
3 or 4 small logs
pitcher of milk
bowl of grapes
small crock of honey
4 plates and knives
4 cups
loaf of bread and knife on
    a board by the hearth
small bench by hearth
5 small chairs or stools
cupboard
table
small chest
hearth

COSTUMES:
BAUCIS and PHILEMON wear sandals and Greek draperies of
muted colors. The chiton, a wide, floor-length piece of ma-

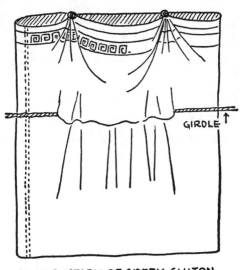

CONSTRUCTION OF GREEK CHITON

terial, is fastened on the shoulders, softly draped, and belted in at the waist. A border design is drawn or embroidered around the edge. The Greek himation is also worn.

JUPITER and MERCURY both wear the short chiton, reaching only to the middle of the thigh; and the chlamys, a small rectangular shawl, shorter than the himation, worn over one shoulder. The clothing is richer in material and brighter in color than the draperies worn by the old couple.

The WOMEN VILLAGERS wear only the long chitons, but the MEN wear both long and short chitons. Dull colors and soft materials should be chosen. Both the himation and chlamys have the Greek border design.

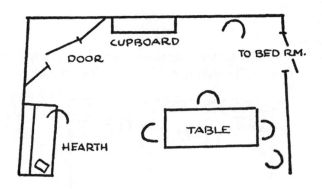

TRAVELERS FROM OLYMPUS

BORROWED TROUBLE

A Danish Legend

THE OBSTINACY of man has often been the basis for comedy; and in this folk tale from Denmark, we find it used to create a conflict between husband and wife. A borrowed pancake griddle, which both refuse to return to the owner, causes them to stop speaking and to sit on opposite sides of the room, regardless of who comes or what happens. The appearance of a coachman, and then his master, the squire, at length brings an end to the quarrel and determines which of the two shall return the griddle.

CHARACTERS

HANS, *the shoemaker*
MAREN, *his wife*
THE SQUIRE
HIS COACHMAN
THE ANNOUNCER

SCENE: *Kitchen of the shoemaker's cottage*

BORROWED TROUBLE

THE PLAY, in one scene, takes place in the kitchen of the shoemaker's cottage. A door U.L. leads to the outside. A wide, open hearth is D.R. A spinning wheel and stool stand at the upper end of the hearth. A table with two chairs, against the wall U.C., and a rough workbench and cupboard D.L. complete the meager furnishings. The table is set for two, with a platter of pancakes in the middle; an iron griddle lies on the floor by the hearth; and shoes, leather, and tools are scattered on the workbench.

❖　❖　❖　❖

ANNOUNCER. (*Comes out in front of curtain to speak.*) There was once, in a small Danish village, an old shoemaker named Hans. He and his wife, Maren, lived happily together, except for the rare occasions when they quarreled. And when that happened, one was as obstinate as the other. Our play takes place in their kitchen one evening as Hans and Maren are just sitting down to supper. There is only one scene, and the other characters who appear in it are the Squire and his Coachman.

(*The* ANNOUNCER *bows and exits. The* CURTAINS *open.* HANS *and* MAREN *are seated at the table U.C.*)

HANS. What a huge platter of pancakes, wife! For once, I shall eat all I can hold!

(*He helps himself to several, then passes the platter to his wife.*)

MAREN. (*Helping herself.*) I have not been unwilling to bake them, Hans. As you know, we have had no pan large enough. And when you asked for cakes, there was nothing in the house to cook them in. This pan is our neighbor's.

HANS. (*Eating rapidly.*) What has become of the griddle that used to hang by the fireplace? The old iron one?

(*When he finishes one cake, he helps himself at once to another.*)

87

MAREN. Do you not remember, Hans, the day that the handle came off, and it fell on the hearthstones and broke?

HANS. So that was it! I remember. Ah, well! It served us for many a meal. (*Pauses a moment while he eats.*) Where did you say you found this?

MAREN. It's borrowed—from our neighbor next door.
(*She, too, goes on eating.*)

HANS. We must get a new pan of our own—one that holds as much batter as this.

MAREN. What a greedy one you are!

HANS. No more than the next man. Each of us has his favorite dish.

MAREN. (*Looking at the diminishing platter with astonishment.*) How quickly they melt away! You eat them in less time than it takes them to cook!

HANS. If there is one thing I like for my supper, it's a platter piled high with good cakes!
(*He helps himself to some more.*)

MAREN. So one would judge by the sight of you.

HANS. True, my dear Maren. I have never tasted better. (*Handing the platter to her.*) Won't you have another?

MAREN. No, thank you, Hans. I have had enough. These pancakes were baked especially for you.

HANS. Good old Maren! Faithful wife! Very well, then, I shall clean them up! (*And he takes another cake.*) Bread and butter, cabbage, steaming hot soup are all very well (*he takes a bite, then continues*), but there's not a meal in all Denmark to compare with this plateful of cakes!
(*And he goes on eating.*)

MAREN. It's a good thing your appetite does not run to roasts and red wine. You would have to make shoes for richer folk than live in this village if it did.

HANS. We live well enough. (*Takes a bite.*) And what little comes in from my cobbling supplies all our wants and needs.

MAREN. For whom are those shoes, Hans? The ones on your workbench?

HANS. Those? (*Looks at them.*) Oh, those are the Squire's. They must be finished tonight. He'll be sending for them later on.

MAREN. Is there much more to do on them?

HANS. Just one sole. And then polish them up a bit. Not so much.

MAREN. Well, then, when you've finished your supper, the pan must be returned to our neighbor. They may need it tonight themselves.

HANS. Go along with it, wife. You may take it back now while I'm smoking my pipe.

(*He pushes back his plate, and walks D.R. to the fireplace to get his pipe.*)

MAREN. I take it back? I take it back, indeed! And why should I return what is borrowed while you smoke your pipe?

HANS. (*By the fireplace, knocking his pipe against the stone.*) Because it was you who borowed it. Had I gone for the pan, I should return it. Since I did not go, there is no reason why I should be the one to take it back.

MAREN. (*Rising angrily from the table.*) But you asked for the pancakes! We had no griddle large enough to bake all you wanted; so I borrowed that one. (*She points at it there by the fire.*) I went for it—I baked the cakes in it— you ate your fill of them—and now you want me to return it!

HANS. (*Coming back to the table, still calm, as he puffs at his pipe.*) Certainly, Maren. It's a woman's work. I tend to my business—and you tend to yours. Now, get along with it.

MAREN. (*Going up to him angrily.*) Indeed I will not! I dislike returning things that are borrowed; and after all you have eaten, you can hardly say that supper is a woman's business!

HANS. (*Beginning to grow angry now, also.*) Maren, I

am losing my patience! These shoes are to finish. The Squire will be coming in a little while and—

MAREN. (*Interrupting him.*) It won't take you ten minutes to run down the lane with that pan!

HANS. I daresay not, my good wife—if I were to do it! But as I have no intention of going, it will take me no time at all!

(HANS *walks over to his workbench, picks up his tools and a shoe, sits, and begins to work.*)

MAREN. (*Stamping her foot in fury.*) Oh! You obstinate, selfish old man! I keep your house, I cook for you, I work hard every day! And then you refuse to do a simple thing like—

HANS. (*Rises in exasperation.*) Maren, will you keep still?

MAREN. I will not!

HANS. How can I work with you shouting at me?

MAREN. There is one way you can get me to stop!

HANS. No, Maren. For the last time, I will not take back the pan!

MAREN. And I will not take it back!

HANS. Then let us make a bargain. We'll say no more about it. Indeed, since talking will only lead to an argument, let us say nothing at all.

MAREN. (*Sullenly.*) Very well.

HANS. And the first one who speaks will return the pan to its owner.

MAREN. (*Rather pleased at the settlement.*) As you say, Hans.

(*She seats herself at her spinning wheel on the hearth, and begins to work industriously.* HANS *returns to his bench and goes after his shoes as if his life depended on it. Several moments pass, and still neither speaks. They glance in the direction of each other occasionally, but turn quickly back to their tasks. At length, there is a* KNOCK *at the door. Both start, but neither will go.*

There is a SECOND KNOCK; *then the door opens, and the Squire's* COACHMAN *comes in.)*

COACHMAN. *(Looking curiously at the old couple.)* Well, I had thought there was no one home! My master wanted his shoes, and so I thought I could get them and then pay you later. *(He walks over to* HANS.*)* Hello! Hello there, shoemaker! *(There is a pause.)* I say, have you both grown deaf since I stopped last? *(Another pause.)* My master needs his shoes! What is the cost of repairing them? *(*HANS *does not reply, but begins to* WHISTLE *softly.)* I say, what is the cost? I can make nothing of whistling! Is this some riddle I'm supposed to guess? Or are you making sport of me? *(Still no reply.)* Does this whistling mean something to you both? *(The* COACHMAN *gives up and walks over to* MAREN. *She begins to hum when he comes near her.)* How is it your husband does not answer when I speak to him? *(A pause.)* Is it that both of you have lost your wits? *(No reply.)* It would seem so. Or is this humming a message of some sort? *(No reply.)* To him? *(No reply.)* To me? *(No reply. He glances from one to the other.)* The man whistles, and his wife sings! And that is all I can make of them! Well, since neither of you will talk, I can do no business here. I must go back to the carriage and tell the Squire what strange thing has happened.

(He turns and walks to the door, then stops, looks at them curiously, taps his head, and goes on out. HANS *and* MAREN *glare at each other, but still neither will give in. After a few moments, there is another* RAP *on the door. This time, it is sharp and imperative. The guest does not wait to knock a second time, but comes in. It is the* SQUIRE *himself, and he is very angry.)*

SQUIRE. Well, so you *are* at home, as my coachman told me! *(Walking over to* HANS.*)* I say, Hans, are the shoes ready? *(*HANS *nods but does not reply. Then the* SQUIRE *shouts.)* Are the shoes ready? *(A pause.)* Not speaking, eh? Well, I can hardly believe that deafness has struck you in a week's time! It was last Saturday I left these, and your tongue was wagging freely enough then! (HANS *glares, and* MAREN *sings more merrily than ever. The* SQUIRE *hears her, and walks across the room to her.*) Nor can I believe that the same affliction has come upon you, my good woman! (*Bending down.*) Can you tell me what ails your husband, eh? (MAREN *is startled, but says nothing.*) Or is this some new kind of insolence that you use on your customers? Faith, it will not bring in much business! (*He walks back to* HANS, *angrier than before.*) Since you won't say what the cost is of repairing, I shall just take these along without paying!

(*He snatches them from* HANS, *who is furious, but manages to control himself. Then the* SQUIRE *crosses back to the wife, and raises his riding whip as he speaks.*) As for you, my good woman, if you are making fun of my coachman and me, I shall teach you some manners! (*He strikes her sharply on the shoulders, but she only sings more loudly.*) So you still won't speak, eh? Very well, then, I shall have to *make* you utter a sound!

(*With this, he strikes her again on the shoulders. She flinches, but does not cry out. It is too much for* HANS, *however. He jumps up and grabs the whip from the* SQUIRE'S *hand.*)

HANS. Stop! Stop it at once! What sort of squire are you that you would whip a defenseless old woman? Take your shoes and get out!

SQUIRE. So! You are not dumb, after all! I am glad to see that your voice has returned to you.

MAREN. (*Laughing, she gets up.*) Ha, ha! Husband, you were the one to speak first! You must take the pan back to our neighbor!

(*Sheepishly,* HANS *crosses to the fireplace to pick up the pan, and, without a word, goes out the door with it under his coat. The* SQUIRE, *now understanding, and* MAREN, *triumphant, stand in the center of the room, laughing heartily as the* CURTAINS *close.*)

TYPICAL DANISH BORDER PATTERNS

Production Notes

PROPERTIES:

griddle
2 plates
2 mugs
platter of pancakes
cutlery for 2
3 or 4 shoes
pieces of leather, lacing, etc.
tools, hammer sewing materials
wool for spinning wheel
riding whip
pipe
fireplace
spinning wheel
stool
2 kitchen chairs
small bench
cupboard

COSTUMES:

MAREN wears a long, full skirt of bright colors, a white peasant blouse with big sleeves, a bodice, an apron, and a small, close-fitting cap. HANS is dressed in knee-length breeches, a white peasant blouse, and bolero. The COACH-MAN appears in knee-length breeches, a short coat, and soft, broad-brimmed hat. The SQUIRE is in knee-length breeches and a longer coat reaching to, or just above, the knee. He also wears a vest and either a soft tie or stock, and a broad-brimmed hat. He carries a riding whip.

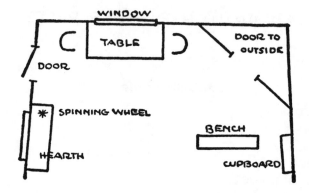

BORROWED TROUBLE

THE LITTLE SQUIRE OF FLANDERS

A French Legend

THIS is a story of friendship, adventure, and mistaken identity. Sir Robert, who has just been knighted and —on the same day—married to the fair Genevieve, is bound to an ancient promise. Long ago he vowed that he would make a pilgrimage to Saint James if ever he were knighted. Now the time has come, and he must leave his newly acquired riches and bride. In the year he is away, there is treason at the castle; and he believes himself exiled forever as the master. During the seven years of wandering which follow, he is joined by a young lad whose devotion and service as his squire bring on better days. Deciding to revisit the castle, he discovers that his squire is in reality his wife, and that it is she who has overcome the evils that beset their path.

CHARACTERS

THE ANNOUNCER

SIR ROBERT, *the new knight and bridegroom*

SIR FRANCOIS, *Genevieve's father*

SIR BERNARD, *a dishonest knight*

GENEVIEVE, *the bride*

PIERRE, *Francois' squire*

YVETTE
MARIE }*Ladies in waiting*
JEANNE

LITTLE JACQUES, *a tumbler*

KNIGHTS AND LADIES IN SCENE 1

SCENE 1: *The castle of Sir Robert.*

SCENE 2: *A road through the forest; a year later.*

SCENE 3: *The castle of Sir Robert; seven years afterward.*

THE LITTLE SQUIRE OF FLANDERS

THE SCENE is the castle of SIR ROBERT *and* GENEVIEVE. *There is a large entrance U.R.C., and a door to another part of the castle D.L. (omitted from diagram on p. 110). Two large chairs at L., a bench against the rear wall, and a fireplace on wall R., with another bench in front of it, are the only pieces of furniture necessary. Everything is heavy and simple—with candelabras, shields, and tapestries to suggest the medieval period in Flanders. The scene may be simplified to the use of only benches and chairs; however, the use of the decorative elements—fleur-de-lis motif and rich colors—will add to the atmosphere.*

❖   ❖   ❖   ❖

ANNOUNCER. Many centuries ago in Flanders there was a young knight dubbed Sir Robert. In his youth he had taken a vow to make a pilgrimage to Saint James, if ever he became a knight. When our play opens, it is both the occasion of his being knighted and his wedding day. The festivities are going on. The characters who appear in this legend are: Robert; Genevieve, his young wife; Sir Francois, her father; Sir Bernard, a dishonest knight; Pierre, a squire; Jacques, a tumbler; Yvette, Marie, and Jeanne—ladies in waiting; and guests at the wedding. There are three scenes. The first and third are in the main room of the castle.

(*He bows and leaves. The* CURTAINS *open on a scene of gaiety, with knights and ladies in the room.* ROBERT *and* GENEVIEVE *are on their throne-like chairs, and servants are in attendance.* ROBERT *is sitting on the right; and* GENEVIEVE, *on the left.* FRANCOIS *is talking with guests before the fireplace, and* BERNARD *is sulking in the rear entrance.*)

FRANCOIS. (*Raising his hand to speak to the group assembled.*) This is a happy day for me. Sir Robert, whom I have known since his childhood, is now knighted and master of this castle. My own squire he was for seven years,

97

and no man has ever had a more faithful friend and servant. Through his bravery and virtue, his toil and devotion to me, he has gained this estate—once part of my own. And he has won also my daughter, the fair Genevieve, who sits by his side. In all of France there is no one I would rather have for a son. And it makes me happy indeed to put my trust in his future.

ALL. (*Applauding and cheering.*) Vive Robert! Vive Genevieve!

ROBERT. (*Rising and coming forward.*) Thank you, Sir Francois. I also have had a faithful companion. And the years ahead must hold great happiness if they would match the years in your service. For your generosity, your love, and your daughter—I am grateful. She alone, whom I had worshipped for seven years, would have been reward enough. But a castle! A title! And esteem! For these I thank you, Sir Francois, and cry with all my heart, "Vive Francois! Vive la France!"

ALL. (*Applauding and cheering again.*) Vive Francois! Vive la France!

FRANCOIS. Thank you, my son. And now let us have music and dancing! Pierre! Pierre! (*Looking about the room.*) Where is my squire?

PIERRE. (*Appearing with a musical instrument—a fiddle or a flute.*) Here I am, my lord.

FRANCOIS. Give us some music, boy! Such as you play for me evenings on your way home from battle.

GENEVIEVE. Yes! Sing to us, Pierre!

ROBERT. Let us have music!

BERNARD. That's it, boy! A song!

JEANNE. Please sing, Pierre.

(*Everyone starts calling for music. There is a hubbub of clapping and calls—"Yes! Yes! Some music! Play for us!" Etc.*)

PIERRE. (*Modestly.*) Very well, my lord. (*To the others.*)

I am not a minstrel, but I have helped pass the long nights for my master when we have been far from home. Here is one of his favorite songs.

(*He plays and sings the "Old French Song." He may either play or sing the melody, or both; but when he is finished, all clap in appreciation. He bows graciously and retires again to his place in the doorway.*)

OLD FRENCH SONG

TRADITIONAL

YOU KNIGHTS OF THE TABLE ROUND, TASTE TO SEE IF THE WINE IS GOOD. YOU TASTE TO

SEE, YES, YES, YES! TASTE TO SEE, NO, NO, NO! TASTE TO SEE IF THE WINE IS GOOD. TASTE TO

SEE, YES, YES, YES! TASTE TO SEE, NO, NO, NO! TASTE TO SEE IF THE WINE IS GOOD.

FRANCOIS. And now, my little Jacques! Where are you, boy? Some tricks for us, eh?

(*At this, a small* CLOWN—*merry, brightly colored, and slightly deformed—runs in at D.L. doorway. He darts to the open space C., and bows low. He does not speak, but dances, spins, and tumbles until the assemblage shouts with laughter. When he has done his dance, he, too, bows and bows again, then runs out the door through which he entered. All applaud heartily.*)

FRANCOIS. (*Calling after him.*) Well done, little Jacques! (*To the others.*) Twenty years he has been in my castle, and he has never yet failed to delight my guests. He is yours, Robert! For he loves my daughter and has amused her for hours on end as a child. He would not be happy away from her—though I shall miss his antics, I know.

ROBERT. You are good, sir. To me and to him. I will take care of the faithful little Jacques as long as he lives.

FRANCOIS. (*As* PIERRE *whispers to him.*) They tell me
the feast is prepared. So let us go into the dining hall
and toast my daughter and my newly gained son. Come,
Robert, Genevieve, lead the way!

(*The young* COUPLE *lead the way out the main entrance
and off L., with the other* LORDS *and* LADIES *following.
All are laughing and talking as they exit.* PIERRE *is last
to go, and the only persons remaining behind are* YVETTE,
MARIE, *and* JEANNE. *They move D.L.C. to whisper
excitedly together.*)

YVETTE. Now, what is it you had to tell, Jeanne?

MARIE. Yes, do hurry, for I do not want to miss the celebration.

YVETTE. There will not be another wedding soon.

MARIE. (*Giggling.*) Unless it be your own, Jeanne. Pierre
has not taken his eyes off your face this whole evening. And
when he sang!—La la!

JEANNE. How you talk! (*Pretending to be annoyed.*) Why,
I have hardly spoken to him at all.

MARIE. But when you did! We were watching, Jeanne, in
the hallway. Whispering and telling secrets—

JEANNE. But that is what I have to tell you now. He told
me— Oh, it is great news!

YVETTE. Well, do let us know, then. They have all gone
in (*nodding toward the dining hall impatiently*), and there
is laughing and noise. I should like to see what is going on.

JEANNE. If you will stop talking long enough. Very well.
(*They listen attentively, and* JEANNE *looks about the room
to be sure they are alone.*) Pierre told me that he overheard
Robert talking with Friar Paul, and he said years ago he—
Robert, that is—made a vow to Saint James to go on a
pilgrimage to his tomb if ever he—Robert, I mean—became
a knight. Now, he has been knighted and married on the
same day, and he—Robert—will have to carry out his vow!
But nobody else knows about it—even Sir Francois—and

he'll probably leave tonight. Now, isn't that the most exciting thing you've ever heard?

MARIE. Jeanne, do you know that for the truth?

JEANNE. Pierre told me! And he heard every word of the conversation between——

YVETTE. Well, I don't think he had any business telling you. Suppose it got back to Sir Francois before Robert had told him? A fine squire Pierre is!

MARIE. I don't think it's exciting—it's dreadful! How many others do you suppose he has told?

JEANNE. None! (*Pouting.*) And I think you're mean not to be interested when I broke my promise to Pierre and told you.

MARIE. Well, I am interested—only I don't think Pierre has any right to go around telling everyone things that he——

JEANNE. But he hasn't told everyone! Just me—and after all, when I said that I'd marry him, I guess——

YVETTE. Jeanne!

MARIE. Marry him! When?

JEANNE. (*Stricken when she realizes that she has told this bit of news.*) Oh, dear, now I've gone and told you all about it; and that was really a secret!

YVETTE. When did he ask you? Tonight?

MARIE. Did you say, "Yes," right away?

YVETTE. But does Sir Francois know? And how can you make any plans for a long, long time, without——

JEANNE. Oh, we can't; and we haven't! And don't you ever tell anybody that I told you! Because he's just a squire—and I'm a lady in waiting without any dowry except what Lady Genevieve gives me—and—oh dear, oh dear! Now, I've gone and spoiled everything!

MARIE. No, you haven't.

YVETTE. We won't tell. But now let us go into the back hall and watch the guests at the banquet.

(The three run out the D.L. entrance and disappear, giggling again. As they leave, ROBERT and GENEVIEVE enter through the main entrance and come down near the fireplace to talk.)

GENEVIEVE. But what did you mean, my lord, about going off tonight? Surely, on your wedding day—

ROBERT. Dear Genevieve, I should have told you before; but I could not. There have been so many around all the time, and with the knighting and wedding on the same day—

GENEVIEVE. *(Interrupting.)* But does my father know?

ROBERT. He does not. Only Friar Paul—I told him this morning. Sit down and let me explain to you. *(She sits on the bench by the fireplace and listens quietly.)* You see, many years ago when I was a boy, I swore that if I became a knight, I should make a pilgrimage to Saint James. There was nothing I wanted so much in the world as to be a knight. Now that my prayer has been answered, I must keep my promise. Neither you nor Sir Francois would want me to break that vow.

GENEVIEVE. No, my lord. *(A pause.)* But must you go at once? Could you not wait for a year—six months? A fortnight at least?

(BERNARD has come to the door D.L., and stands listening to the conversation.)

ROBERT. No, my dear. It is now. I must go as I promised. But in a year—or less—I shall come back. You will wait for me, won't you?

BERNARD. *(Coming forward with a sneer.)* She will be here, no doubt. But if your place in her heart is not filled, I shall give up all my lands and my riches.

ROBERT. *(Starting at the sound of BERNARD'S voice.)* Sir Bernard! What I am saying to my wife is for her ears alone!

GENEVIEVE. And she will keep faith. His place in her heart will be waiting.

ROBERT. That I know, Genevieve. And it gives me courage to go.

BERNARD. I envy your confidence, my lord. When do you set out?

ROBERT. At once. (*Demanding of* BERNARD.) Will you leave us?

BERNARD. Of course. (*Sneering.*) May I wish you a good journey? Since I do not expect to see one so foolhardy return, let me congratulate you now on your good fortune! (*With a low, mocking bow, he goes out.*)

ROBERT. Genevieve, we must go back now and tell your father.

GENEVIEVE. Whatever happens, my lord, I shall be faithful —and waiting.
(*As they turn to go back through the large entrance at C., the* CURTAINS *close.*)

SCENE TWO

This scene is a lonely road leading through a forest. There are logs scattered about, trees and bushes, and a campfire by which ROBERT *is sitting, eating his supper. Space before the main curtains may be used for this, to simplify the "scenery" problem. In such an event, the campfire would have to become purely an imaginary one. If footlights are used, their illumination will help to create the illusion, as Robert sits on the floor, facing them. It is dark, for evening is approaching.*

❖   ❖   ❖   ❖

ANNOUNCER. It is a year later. Sir Robert has made his pilgrimage; but upon his return to the castle, he was told that Bernard had become master in his place—that Genevieve had given him up—and that Sir Francois had taken back his gifts. Weary and unhappy, the young knight turned his steps to the forest. It is here we find him alone by the fire.

(*The* ANNOUNCER *bows and leaves, and the* CURTAINS *open to show* ROBERT *by the fire. If the scene is played before the main curtain,* ROBERT *can enter and pantomime the building of a small campfire as he speaks.*)

ROBERT. (*Sighing.*) Lord of a castle but a year ago! With a beautiful wife and wealth for my seven years of service. Now I can claim nothing—nothing but my honor. For the vow has been kept, and my pilgrimage is over.

(*He takes a roll of bread from his bag and begins eating it. After a moment, a young lad comes along. The boy known here as* GUILLAUME—*is* GENEVIEVE *in disguise. She wears boy's clothes, and has tucked her hair under a cap. Her face is smeared with a dark paint.* ROBERT *does not recognize her at all.*)

GUILLAUME. (*Stepping up to* ROBERT *and speaking.*) Are you traveling alone, sir?

ROBERT. (*Startled at the sound of a voice.*) Why, yes, lad! What are you doing in the forest with night coming on?

GUILLAUME. Looking for a master, my lord. I am a poor squire with no one to serve; and when I saw you, I thought if—I thought if . . .

ROBERT. (*Sadly.*) If I needed a squire, I might take you along? (*He smiles, then shakes his head.*) I am without a squire—but I am also without a sou. And I could pay you nothing for your service.

GUILLAUME. (*Gently.*) Could you not pay me in friendship, my lord? I, too, am alone in the world now. And I would rather share your adventures than seek those of my own. Please let me stay with you.

ROBERT. (*Becoming interested.*) What is your name, my lad?

GUILLAUME. Guillaume, sir.

ROBERT. Guillaume. (*Pauses.*) And if my road leads away from Flanders?

GUILLAUME. (*Simply.*) I am without a master, sir. I will follow where you go.

ROBERT. Then sit down and have bread with me. There is not much for our supper.

(*Hands a roll to* GUILLAUME. *Both eat.*)

GUILLAUME. I have fruit—and a few gold coins that my father left me. (*Handing them to* ROBERT.) Take them, my lord, and use them for us both.

ROBERT. (*Refusing them.*) But I cannot spend your coins, my boy.

GUILLAUME. We must get started. And if there are a few coins between us, why not use them?

ROBERT. But they are yours!

GUILLAUME. If I am your squire, then what is mine belongs to you also. Take them, my lord.

(*He again presses them on* ROBERT.)

ROBERT. (*Taking the coins as he thinks aloud.*) I was thinking, Guillaume, before you came along . . . . There is a shop for sale in a village near by. If I were to take it and sell bread and cakes— But I had no money to buy—

GUILLAUME. (*His eyes sparkling.*) Then I could help you! For I learned how to bake from my mother's cook. I remember—although I've not been in a kitchen for years—I remember how it was done. Let us buy the shop with this gold. And I will bake and help you sell the bread for a profit.

ROBERT. But can you do all these things, little squire?

GUILLAUME. All these and more! For I learned much at the castle—from the kitchen to the tournaments—and I know an honorable man from a dishonest one.

ROBERT. Very well, Guillaume. We shall set out for that village in the morning. We will buy the shop with your gold, and we'll seek our fortune together. (*Yawns and gets up.*) I am afraid that tonight our bed must be the hard ground. Soon we shall do better. Can you sleep here by the fire?

GUILLAUME. Of course, my lord. Here! I shall spread my

cloak on this side and put yours over there. (*He quickly and deftly spreads the two cloaks on either side of the fire.*) Now we shall each get the warmth of the fire and yet have soft wool beneath us.

ROBERT. (*Admiringly.*) Guillaume, you are wiser than your years. How does it happen?

GUILLAUME. (*Very simply.*) Because I have you to serve. Devotion to one's master makes one think of many things.

(ROBERT *smiles in appreciation; then the two lie down on their cloaks, and the* CURTAINS *close slowly. Again, if the scene is in front of the curtain, they may walk out D.R., or wait until the footlights are off and leave quietly.*)

SCENE THREE

THE FIRST-Scene set is brought again into use.

* * * * *

ANNOUNCER. Seven years have passed. During this time, the little squire, Guillaume, served his master faithfully and well. They bought the shop, and they sold bread and cakes until they grew wealthy. Finally, Robert decided that with money in his pocket he should become a knight again. He wanted to take the little squire with him and go off to distant lands. But for the first time, Guillaume begged him to do otherwise. Now that Robert was a rich knight, he insisted, it would do no harm to return to his castle. There were those who might like to see him; and, anyhow, it would do no harm. So Robert parted from his little friend and went back. But to his astonishment, Bernard, who had usurped his place, was gone on a last pilgrimage for his sins. Francois welcomed him home; and his wife, Genevieve, was waiting for her master. It is here that we find him.

(*He bows and leaves. The* CURTAINS *open.* ROBERT *and* GENEVIEVE *are seated in the two chairs, where we saw them at the beginning of the play. The three ladies in waiting are in the room near the entrance, and* PIERRE *is at the D.L. doorway.* FRANCOIS, *now looking much older, is sitting on the bench by the fire.*)

JEANNE. (*With a curtsy.*) It is good to have you home again, my lord.

YVETTE. (*With a curtsy.*) And you, too, my lady. It has been strange and not happy in this castle all these years.

MARIE. (*With a curtsy.*) Ill luck began the night of your wedding—and has dwelt among us ever since. But now, begging you pardon, it is gone with Sir Bernard. We are glad you are back!

ROBERT. Thank you all! And yet, do you know, everyone and everything looks just as it did when I left?

GENEVIEVE. (*Turning to her husband.*) Tell us more of your adventures, my husband. Seven years has been a long, long time.

ROBERT. Well, two years after we had set up the bakeshop we took over an inn. Little Guillaume was as skilled at accounts as he was at the baking. Everything we did turned into profit. He did twice as much work as I—and when I asked him why he took such pains for me, he said, "When you were a squire, my lord, did you regret the trouble you took for your master?"

FRANCOIS. And where is the boy now, Robert?

ROBERT. That is what troubles me, sir. I left him in the village. I must let him know how things have come out, and bring him home to the castle. (*Pause.*) But now you must tell me what has happened here in the years I've been gone.

FRANCOIS. Only sorrow, my boy. When Bernard reported you dead, I was ill and could not find out the truth for myself. When I was able to seek you, there was no one to say you were living. Genevieve——

GENEVIEVE. I went away then, my lord, on a quest of my own.

107

FRANCOIS. A convent where she could pray for her husband. She, too, has just come home again. Strange— you gone for eight years, she for seven—that both should choose the same day to return! But, then, the ways of the Lord are strange, and we do not understand.

(*Shakes his head.*)

GENEVIEVE. (*Hurriedly.*) And then Bernard—I would not marry him—but he took this place just the same—

FRANCOIS. And now he is gone on a last pilgrimage to the Holy Land. When sickness came, he was not ready—and must repent of his sins.

GENEVIEVE. So the pieces are put together! We shall have a happy life, Robert, even though it is beginning seven years later than we had thought.

FRANCOIS. (*Rises. All rise when he does.*) If you will excuse an old man, I will leave you. I am not equal to the banquets and celebrations of the past. (PIERRE *waits for him to walk to the door D.L., where he pauses for a moment.*) Good night, my lord. Good night, my child.

(*He and* PIERRE *go out.* GENEVIEVE *looks at the three ladies in waiting, and dismisses them.*)

GENEVIEVE. You may go—Jeanne, Yvette, Marie. Come to me in the morning as usual.

(*They curtsy and go out at C. There is a moment of silence; then* ROBERT *walks down to the fireplace and stands by it, his back to his wife. After a moment she speaks.*)

GENEVIEVE. (*Very gently.*) What is it, my lord, that makes you unhappy? Everything has been restored to you—your castle, your riches, your wife. What more can you want than is here?

ROBERT. (*Hesitantly, after a pause.*) There's one thing. And I am bound to go after it.

GENEVIEVE. What is that, my lord?

ROBERT. My little squire, Guillaume. I left him, intending to return at once. Now that things have changed, I must find him and tell him. I want him to come here if he will. But until I have seen Guillaume, believe me, I cannot eat or sleep!

GENEVIEVE. (*Very quietly.*) Does that mean, my lord, that you love him better than me?

ROBERT. To tell you the truth, Genevieve, I do not know. You are my wife, but he was my friend! For seven years he has served me. We were happy together. I wish I had not to choose between you.

GENEVIEVE. Must you, my lord? (*Looks at him intently.*) Must you choose?

ROBERT. (*Looking at her closely for the first time.*) You ... Genevieve—Guillaume—I have hardly looked at you till now . . . and in these clothes . . .

GENEVIEVE. (*Smiling.*) If you would like, my lord, I will dress in the others again, and rub my face with the stain that took so long to get off.

ROBERT. (*Wondering.*) My faithful squire! My loyal wife! To have both in one!

GENEVIEVE. (*Teasing him.*) But now you cannot complain about your wife to your squire—nor criticize your squire to your wife!

ROBERT. (*With great admiration.*) There will be no need to do either. How few men have such good fortune! Surely this is worth the waiting—for seven long years!

(*They smile at each other as the* CURTAINS *close.*)

Production Notes

PROPERTIES:
   musical instrument (flute, harp or guitar)
   2 rolls (bakery)
   several gold coins
   fireplace
   2 large chairs
   fire

2 long benches
trees or bushes (optional)

COSTUMES:

The MEN wore tights, soft shoes, and long capes. Doublets
were either with or without sleeves. If without, there was
always another garment with sleeves underneath. Older
men often wore the knee-length cote-hardie. Colors were
brilliant during the late Gothic period. Reds, blues, greens
and golds were interspersed with duller shades of browns
and grays. Patterns and plain colors were both used.

The LADIES wore tight, high-waisted bodices and full, wide
skirts. Both tight sleeves and long flowing ones were worn.
No headdress was necessary; although the horned headdress
for married women was coming into style. Loose, flowing
hair was popular—especially for young women.

JACQUES wears the jester outfit with knee-length jerkin,
tights, and covered head. It is traditional, and bright in
color. Although many jesters of this period *were* deformed,
it is not necessary to follow this description.

PRONUNCIATION:

Guillaume is pronounced *Gēē'ome.*

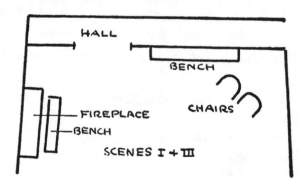

THE LITTLE SQUIRE OF FLANDERS

CHRISTMAS FIESTA

A Mexican Festival

PERHAPS even more picturesque than the legends of Mexico are its customs. And of these, the fiesta is indisputably the most dramatic and colorful. It has been said that there is no day in the year when some town or village is not thronged with people in costume, celebrating a national or religious holiday—having a fiesta. Even the gayest are of a religious nature, yet the most deeply religious have a festive spirit. One occasion which is always celebrated, but particularly by the children, is Christmas. Because this festival is so widespread in its celebration, so charming, and so truly Mexican in feeling, it is included as a bit of folklore which lends itself well to the participation and enjoyment of children everywhere.

CHARACTERS

THE ANNOUNCER

ANSELMO

MARIA, *his wife*

JUAN, *their little boy*

PEDRO, *his younger brother*

ESTABAN, *leader of the group outside for the posada*

PEPE, *leader of the group inside*

LOLA, *a young girl*

GUESTS, *as many as desired, and many children*

SCENE: *The home of Anselmo and his family in a Mexican pueblo.*

TIME: *The present. Christmas Eve.*

CHRISTMAS FIESTA

*C*HRISTMAS FIESTA *may be given as entertainment on a stage, or as a party in which all the children take part. Perhaps only the rôles of Anselmo and Maria should be rehearsed, and the others allowed to join in freely. All would, of course, need to be familiar with the dances that are used, the song that is sung, and the general background of the fiesta. But it might be more spontaneous if it were not rehearsed as to the actual party, at least if done as a simple class project—rather, letting the children participate within the framework. In this way, the production becomes a festival rather than a play—with the emphasis upon costuming, singing, dancing, and the holiday spirit, rather than upon dramatic form and technique.*

*T*HE SCENE *is the simple home of* ANSELMO *and his family in a Mexican pueblo. Since it is Christmas Eve, they are celebrating with a fiesta, to which many other families are invited. The room is a rather large one with a wide door leading to the patio off L. In the U.R. wall is another door to the rest of the house. There is a large, heavy table, laden with food, against the wall R. A long bench is beside it. U.C., against the wall, is a branch of pine mounted on a small table or box. It is decorated with candles and poinsettias, and occupies a position of importance in the room. Beneath it is a crèche, or "nacimiento," as it is called in Mexico. Crude figures of the Holy Family, shepherds and shepherdesses, and the three kings are in the little stable which, of course, cannot be clearly seen from the audience. It is included because it is traditional and because it is used later in the evening. A chair U.R.C. and another chair in the D.L. corner are the only other pieces of furniture.*

* * * * *

ANNOUNCER. (*Coming out in front of curtain.*) It is

113

Christmas Eve. All over the world people are celebrating the season in their own ways. In Mexico there are fiestas —gay parties which are held in the village square, in the church, and in the homes of the people. Since it is a very special occasion for the children, we should like to invite you to a fiesta given by Anselmo and his family. The scene is their house, and the neighbors have already arrived. First there is dancing, then the lighting of the candles, next the posada, which means acting out the story of Mary and Joseph. After that, they have the pinata, a game; and then refreshments are served.

(*The* ANNOUNCER *leaves, and the* CURTAINS *are opened, revealing the room described previously. Candles on the table suggest evening, and the guests have already gathered. The door to the patio is open, and just outside can be seen two or three* MUSICIANS *playing guitars or mandolins and a drum. The* GUESTS *inside are dancing a Mexican folk dance, and as many may take part as desired. The children watch from the D.L. and D.R. corners, and the doorway. A simple group dance comes first. The guests, when it is over, move to positions around the edges of the room while a couple come forward to do a dance for two.—This can be omitted; but if there are two children who dance well, it will add variety to the program. See Production Notes.—When the dancing is over,* ANSELMO *steps to the center of the room and calls loudly. He is holding a candle in his hand.*)

ANSELMO. Maria! Maria! The candles for our guests!

MARIA. (*Coming to his side with a basket of red, green, and white candles.*) Here, Anselmo, red ones, green ones, and white ones. A candle for each!
(*She moves about the room quickly, giving a candle to each person.*)

PEDRO. I did not get one!

MARIA. Have patience, Pedro! There are enough for all!
—(*She tosses one to him.*)

114

JUAN. And I, Mamma. You did not give me one either!

MARIA. What children! As if I would leave you out! There! (*She tosses another to* JUAN.) Now, has everyone a candle?

(*Everyone answers her at once, ad libbing their lines as follows:* "Yes, Maria! We have! I have! Yes, yes!" *etc.*)

MARIA. Very well then, we shall receive the sacred fire. Anselmo!

ANSELMO. Yes, Maria. With you, I shall begin.

(*He lights her candle. After hers is lighted, they both turn to light those of their nearest neighbors; and they, in turn, light the candles nearest them. Thus, no one lights his own, but each has received the fire from another. Soon all the candles are lighted. When this has been done,* ANSELMO *moves again to a central position and announces the next part of the program.*)

ANSELMO. With our lighted candles let us have a posada! Estaban, you will go with the procession. You, Pepe, stay inside. All on this side of the room join Estaban. (*He indicates* L. *side.*) All on this side stay here with Pepe. Maria, bring the images. (*Turns to the group at* L.) You will go to the patio and sing at this door.

(*He indicates the main door* L. MARIA *picks up the images of Joseph and Mary from the nacimiento and brings them to him. He hands one to* ESTABAN *and the other to a* WOMAN *near him.*)

Now, the posada! (*Meaning the room itself.*) This is the inn!

(*With this, the* GROUP *of* PILGRIMS *go with their candles,* LAUGHING *and* TALKING, *out the door; and it is closed. Then* ANSELMO *motions to the others remaining in the room to stand behind him and* PEPE.)

ANSELMO. All of you, here—by Pepe, near the door. Are you ready? The procession with the Holy Family has stopped at every door in the pueblo and now it is coming

here. (*He runs to the door and calls out.*) Are you ready? (*There is a* MUFFLED RESPONSE, *and he turns to his own group again.*) They are ready. Now, let us sing!
(*They sing back and forth several verses of "The Pilgrims," in which those outside beg to be let in. The group inside act out the haughty innkeepers who are disdainful of guests. Finally, at the end of the last verse,* PEPE *opens the door, and the* PROCESSION *is welcomed. The posada is over. There is excitement again, laughing and talking. The candles, which by now are burned down, are put out. Once again* ANSELMO *shouts to his* GUESTS *from the table R.*)

ANSELMO. A drink for each—and the pinata!
(MARIA, PEPE, *and* ESTABAN *move about with cups, which are taken by the guests and quickly drained.* ANSELMO *goes out the U.R. door and reappears immediately with a huge piece of pottery or ornate paper filled with sweets, nuts, and oranges. This is the pinata.*)

ANSELMO. I will hang the pinata here, so all may see it. It is low enough for even the smallest to reach.
(*He hangs it on a hook suspended from the ceiling, in full view. There is another cord beside it with which he can pull the pinata up or down.*)

MARIA. Who would like to try breaking it first? Lola? Favian? Pepe?
(*The guests call to her in ad lib remarks—"Go on, Lola! Lola, you try first!" etc. There is much giggling as a pretty young girl goes to the center of the room and allows herself to be blindfolded by* ANSELMO. MARIA *hands her a stick, and she is then turned around several times. Finally she is released to try her luck at hitting the pinata. There is excitement and amused response as she tries again and again, unsuccessfully. If possible, the pinata can be raised or lowered so that one guest after another fails. When several turns have been taken, the pinata may be broken, and the contents spilled out on the floor.*)

All shout and dive after the candy and nuts. After all have been picked up, MARIA *announces supper, which is already on the table. It is to be a stand-up affair.*)

MARIA. There is supper for all on the table! Dulce! Tostadas! Enchiladas! Tacos! Come, be welcome! There is plenty!

(*All swarm about the table, eating, drinking, and enjoying themselves. Because the Mexican people are formal and polite, they are courteous but, nevertheless, enjoy the occasion. If the play is given on a stage before an audience, it may end at this point. If it is given in the classroom, with all participating, it may simply conclude with the eating of the refreshments by everyone.*)

Production Notes

PROPERTIES:

pine bough decorated with poinsettias
bowls of food on table
cups for all, and pitcher full of a drink for everyone
large candles on table
red, green, and white candles for all
stick
pinata (huge piece of pottery or paper, filled with sweets,
    nuts, oranges)
guitars, mandolins, drum
crèche (stable with crude figures of the Holy Family, shep-
    herds, and the three kings.)
long table
long bench
2 chairs
small table for pine bough
cord or stick with hook, on which to suspend pinata

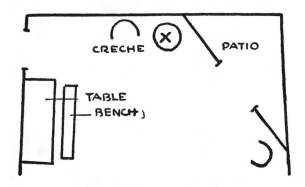

GHRISTMAS FIESTA

COSTUMES:

The women wear full skirts of red, yellow, and blue flowered
materials; low-cut blouses; ribbons or flowers for the hair;
and rebozos or thin black shawls. (The rebozo is a very
long scarf to be wrapped about the head and shoulders.)

The men wear pink, lavender, or white shirts; and white trousers, tighter at the calf and ankle than above. Some of the men wear short leather jackets, and some wear serapes. (The serape is a heavy woven rug of wool with a hole in the middle for the head.)

NOTE: Because lighted candles are frequently impractical with a group of small children, it is suggested that electric candles would work as well. If these are not available, the real candles might be used but not lighted. The action would suggest the custom—with no danger to the participants.

PANTOMIME:

In this pantomime, the children in the room pretend to be haughty and disdainful of the group outside. They go to the door L. when they sing, then, as a group, move D.R. again. They listen to the pleas of those outside, but reject them each time. Finally, when the group outside sing their last verse, the host goes to the door and asks them to enter. They come in, are welcomed, and urged to sit down and join the festivities. Thus the story of the Holy Family's rejection at each door, and eventual permission to take shelter in the stable, is enacted. The procession through the village is simply suggested by this traditional little pantomime and song.

THE DANCE—"El Jarabe":

This dance is suggested because of its popularity and simplicity. Any other, however, could be used. This particular one is found in *Legends and Dances of Old Mexico*, by Norma Schwendener and Averil Tibbels, published by A. S. Barnes and Company, N. Y., 1933.

Music for it is found in *American Indian and Other Folk Dances*, by Mary Severance Shafter, published by A. S. Barnes and Company; also in Columbia Records 2570— X, 95432.

SOME HELP WITH SPANISH WORDS

pueblo (pwĕb' lō): A group of people living together, a village.

pinata (pĭn yä' tä): The game in which the piece of decorated pottery, filled with candies, is broken.

serape (sĕ rä' pē): A garment worn by the men—a rectangular woolen blanket with a hole in the center for the head. Worn over the shoulder as a protection.

crèche (krĕsh): Manger and small figures, elaborately or crudely made of pottery or wood, to represent Mary, Joseph, and the others who were present on the first Christmas in the stable.

Nacimiento (nä cĭmïĕn' tō): The Birth of Jesus.

posada (pō sä' dä): A place to stay, a hostel—in this instance, the *action* involved in the turning away of Mary and Joseph from the inn, and the eventual invitation to enter.

el jarabe (ĕl häräb' ē): One of the oldest folk dances of Mexico, taught to the smallest school children, and most frequently danced at informal parties such as the one described here.

dulce (dōl' sē): Sweets or cakes.

tostadas (tōstä' däs): Mexican food—meats or salads on fried tortillas.

tacos (tä' kōs): Mexican food—chicken, cheese, etc., rolled in a tortilla.

enchiladas (ĕn chĭl ä' däs): Mexican food—fried tacos, covered with sauces of tomatoes and chile, mole or cream.

tortillas (tŏr tēē' yä): Thin corn pancakes.

BIBLIOGRAPHY

Fergusson, Erna, *Fiesta In Mexico*. Knopf, 1934.

Henius, Frank, *Songs and Games of the Americas*. Scribners (New York), 1943.—(*This includes many delightful Mexican games which could be added to this festival, particularly if it is being done as a "party," or with younger children.*)

Meyers, Susanna, *Folk Songs of the Four Seasons*. G. Schirmer, 1929.

Trend, J. B., *Mexico*. Macmillian Company, 1940.

Schwendener and Tibbels, *Legends and Dances of Old Mexico*. A. S. Barnes (New York), 1933.

Shafter, Mary Severance, *American Indian and Other Folk Dances*. A. S. Barnes & Co.

Spratling, William, *Little Mexico*. Jonathan Cape and Harrison Smith, 1932.

THE PILGRIMS

ANDANTINO   MEXICAN

1. TWO WEARY PILGRIMS WE COME TO YOUR DOOR, SHELTER AND COMFORT WE

BEG AND IM — PLORE, NINE DAYS WE'VE JOURNEYED, NOW WE MUST

STAY. OPEN THE PORTAL, O- MAKE NO DE- LAY, NO DE - LAY.

ENTER PILGRIMS, WELCOME PILGRIMS, TO MY DWELLING, OF MY

(CHILDREN'S CHORUS - OPTIONAL)

FAMILY MAKE A PART. 1. CANDY FOR CHRISTMAS, HANDFULS OF

CANDY, PEANUTS AND CHESTNUTS + BASKETS OF CANDY. CANDY.

The Pilgrims

MEXICAN FOLK SONG

1. Two weary pilgrims, we come to your door,
   Shelter and comfort we beg and implore;
   Nine days we've journeyed,
   Now we must stay.
   Open the portal, O make no delay.

2. Ask not admission at this bolted door,
   There is no room here for even one more.
   Trouble me not, with cares I am pressed;
   Come now, be off, and disturb not,
   Disturb not our rest!

3. Nay, but my friend, you must give us your aid;
   Help us, I pray you, and be not afraid.
   Hope has sustained us all through the day;
   Hope of your kindness has brightened,
   Has brightened our way.

Refrain
   Enter pilgrims, welcome pilgrims,
   To my dwelling, of my family make a part.
   Here is shelter, weary pilgrims,
   In my dwelling, and a welcome in my heart.

Children's Chorus (Optional)
1. Candy for Christmas,
   Handfuls of candy,
   Peanuts and chestnuts
   And baskets of candy.

2. Candy for Christmas,
   Please give us candy,
   Pineapple, sweetmeats
   And plenty of candy.

(NOTE: The carol is a dialogue between Joseph and the Innkeeper or the Host, the former singing verses one and three, the latter, verses two and the refrain. The first three verses should be sung through with slight pauses, then the fourth, dramatically, after longer pause. The children's chorus may or may not be used, as desired.)

Found in *Folk Songs of the Four Seasons*, text and translations by Susanna Myers, harmonization by Harvey Officer, published by G. Schirmer, New York. Used by special arrangement with the publishers.

PAUL BUNYAN: LUMBERJACK

An American Legend

A BOOK OF LEGENDS is scarcely complete if it fails to include at least one adventure of the legendary logger of our own Northwest, Paul Bunyan. Although these stories did not appear until the middle of the nineteenth century and later, they are folklore in the truest sense. Paul was a gigantic figure and a man of magnificent deeds. Because he is so recent a creation, the storytellers have all claimed actual acquaintance with him and have vied with one another in the heroics they recall. In this dramatization the techniques of storytelling and acting are combined, since it would be impossible to present the stories in their real magnitude.

CHARACTERS

JOE LARKEY, *the first storyteller, a man of about 60, dressed as a lumberjack*

PETE JOHNSON, *the second storyteller, a somewhat younger man*

OLE, *the blacksmith*

SLIM, *the cook*

DICK LOOMIS, *a logger*

SEVERAL OTHER LOGGERS, *any number*

EIGHT OR TEN BOYS ON ROLLER SKATES

BOY IN AUDIENCE

GIRL IN AUDIENCE

The time is the present, and the action, which takes place in a large open area, is continuous.

PAUL BUNYAN: LUMBERJACK

THE ACTION is continuous as the two storytellers match yarns and the three scenes are enacted. Because the feats of PAUL *are so prodigious, a stage presentation is impossible. Therefore, the storytellers speak from downstage, on the apron if there is one, leaving a large open area behind them. No scenery is necessary but a few properties such as a table and chair will help to suggest the setting. The curtain is not drawn at any point in the play, and even more audience participation than that suggested in the script could be included.*

When the audience is seated, the storyteller, JOE LARKEY, *appears from D.R. He is a man of about sixty, dressed as a lumberjack, and stands R. of C., looking out for a moment before beginning. Then he speaks directly and informally to the audience.*

ᕦ   ᕦ   ᕦ   ᕦ

JOE. Don't know how many of you folks have ever heard of Paul Bunyan in these parts? Or his wonderful blue ox, Babe?

(*He stops and looks out to see whether anyone has.*)

BOY IN AUDIENCE. Sure I have! He was a logger in Minnesota.

GIRL IN AUDIENCE. No, Wisconsin! I read all about him in a book. And his ox, too.

JOE. (*Chuckling.*) Well, you're both right. Some say he came from Michigan and others claim he did his biggest piece of work in South Dakota. Fact is, he was in all those places and cleared more land and felled more trees than any other lumberjack in the whole Northwest. He was a great logger, that's sure, and I guess there wasn't ever anybody else quite like him. (*He steps forward and*

127

continues confidentially.) About where he came from, though, there's some say he was born in Maine; and he was so strong even when he was a little shaver, he knocked down five miles of timber just learning to toddle. 'Course they couldn't have that kind of thing going on, so the government made his folks take him out West where there was plenty of space.

BOY IN AUDIENCE. I read he came over from Canada.

JOE. Well, there's some will tell you that for a fact. I don't recollect Paul ever saying, though. Just saw where there was a job to be done and he did it. Didn't talk about himself much. I knew him first in Wisconsin. That was way back, and Babe, the blue ox, wasn't full-grown yet.

GIRL IN AUDIENCE. How big was he really, the ox?

JOE. Well, now I can't tell you just how big he got to be finally. But that winter he measured forty-two ax handles between the eyes, and a tobacco box.

BOY IN AUDIENCE. Aw, I don't believe it!

JOE. (*Warmly.*) I was there and I saw him! He wasn't like anything else this side of the border. Bright blue with white horns and gentle as a great Dane puppy. (*More matter-of-factly.*) 'Course it took a lot to feed him, but then he got more done in a day than a whole pasture full of ordinary oxen in a week. Used to haul a whole section of timber at a time—six hundred acres cleared in one day.

(*While* JOE *pauses to let this statement be felt, there is a commotion in the audience and another lumberjack comes hurrying down the aisle. This is* PETE JOHNSON, *a younger man, who is dressed in similar clothes. He mounts the stage and crosses over to* JOE.)

PETE. Say, hold on there a minute! I've worked alongside that blue ox myself, and if he couldn't haul off that much timber in one trip between sunset and supper, I'm a——

JOE. (*Interrupting.*) Wait a second, young feller. Where did you know Paul?

PETE. Why, up in Dakota. Biggest camp he ever made. Three winters I took care of that blue ox and fed it. And let me tell you, we had to get ready a whole year ahead of time. Why, four ton of grain was nothing for Babe to eat in one meal!

JOE. (*Stepping up and shaking* PETE's *hand with the friendly recognition of a fellow storyteller.*) Put it there. What's your name, partner? I reckon you're telling the truth.

PETE. (*Smiling now, also.*) Pete Johnson, sir. And yours?

JOE. Joe Larkey. A logger myself from way back.

PETE. Glad to meet you. (*He looks out at the audience for the first time since mounting the stage. Then he turns back to* JOE.) But what are you doing up here?

JOE. Why, I was fixing to tell these folks about Paul. But now you're here, why, maybe you could help me out?

PETE. Sure thing. (*To the audience.*) You see, we fellers that worked with Paul, we can't ever forget him. Why, every time two of us get together we just start talking about him. They don't grow men like that any more. There wasn't a stronger, smarter logger ever lived.

JOE. He had some good men working for him, though. I recollect the time he hired Ole and Slim. It was right after I came. Kind of funny, too—only joke we ever got on Paul. It was like this. We were needing a cook and a blacksmith, both.

(*As he begins to tell it,* OLE *and* SLIM *enter U.L. and come slowly to the center as if looking for someone.*)

Seems as if they'd heard about the jobs and came looking for Paul together.

(*He pauses again and walks a few steps nearer C. so that he is in the scene which is now enacted. At this moment, the gigantic figure of* PAUL BUNYAN *emerges from U.R.C. and moves slowly and with deliberation to C. Although a huge man, there is as much of kindliness in his bearing as there is of power.* PETE *looks on from his position D.R. of the apron.*)

OLE. They say he's a big feller—can't take him for anybody else.

SLIM. Honest, though. A good boss. None of his men ever leaves him.

OLE. Look! There he is! Over there!

(*They stand and watch, somewhat overwhelmed, as* PAUL *and* JOE *talk.*)

PAUL. Well, Joe, I reckon we got a lot to do today. Out there. (*He points out front as if a forest were standing before him.*) Pine, hemlock, and spruce. Forests of 'em. All waiting to be cut.

JOE. And all on the level, too. We can use the big falling saw on this all right.

PAUL. You bet! Had an extra piece put on that saw. Reaches half a mile now! (*He makes a wide gesture as if to suggest the scope of his timber felling.*) Got too much to do to waste time getting at it. The blue ox fed yet?

JOE. Fed and cleaned, sir. Ready to be shod. He's in the blacksmith's shanty now, if there's anybody can shoe him.

(*By this time the two* STRANGERS *have decided to approach the gigantic figure; they walk up to him.*)

OLE. Is this here Paul Bunyan's camp?

PAUL. (*Heartily.*) It is. And who might you be looking for?

OLE. Well, my partner and me—we heard you were needing some help.

(*He presents a card timidly.*)

SLIM. (*Adding his bit.*) Cook and blacksmith, sir. And we're here to find out if——

PAUL. (*Handing the card to* JOE.) What's it say, Joe?

JOE. (*Reading with difficulty.*) Says here they're Ole Lindgren and Slim Weston—good men. One's a blacksmith and the other's a cook.

PAUL. I've been needing more help. The camp's grown. Think you'd like to join up with us, eh?

OLE. Oh, yes, sir. Me, I'm the——

PAUL. (*Laughing and interrupting.*) I can see you're the cook—clean shirt—all spruced up——

OLE. (*Shaking his head.*) But I——

PAUL. (*Pointing off R.*) You go down to that cabin. There's two hundred men will be wanting breakfast right now.

OLE. (*Starting off in the direction indicated, protesting but not yet making himself heard.*) No, sir, he's the—— (*He points frantically at* SLIM.) I say, he's the——

PAUL. (*Has turned his complete attention now to* SLIM.) Might have guessed you were a blacksmith right off. Look like you just stepped out of the forge! Well, now, there's a job for you, too. You can start in right away.

SLIM. But I can't. I'm not the——

PAUL. (*Going right on.*) My blue ox needs a shoe before we can begin hauling timber. He's down there. (*Pointing D.L.*) You'll find him gentle.

(SLIM *starts off in that direction, still trying to explain.*)

SLIM. Yes, but you see, I don't know anything about——

PAUL. You'll find everything there. All the tools you'll be needing. Get along! (PAUL *turns back to* JOE *as* SLIM *disappears D.L.*) Well, now that's what I call luck! The help I need most, and they come walking right into camp.

JOE. (*Doubtfully, indicating the card.*) Better wait and see if they're as good as this says.

PAUL. Won't take long to find out. Here comes the cook

now with his griddle cakes. Pull up a chair and we'll try 'em.

(*The two men seat themselves at the table as* OLE *brings in a platter of cakes.* PAUL *turns to* OLE.) Hope you can turn these out fast, son. There's a lot of hungry men in this camp. Some eat as many as eighty-five in a meal. (PAUL *bites into a cake ravenously and then roars out.*) What did you put in that batter? They're like pieces of iron!

OLE. (*Desperately.*) It's what I've been trying to tell you, sir! I'm the blacksmith! And I never cooked before in my life!

SLIM. (*Running in.*) I can't do it! I just can't do it! I'm quitting! First he kicks me in the head, that blue ox! Then he runs off! I never tried to make a shoe before! I'm a cook!

PAUL. (*Rising from the table and roaring with laughter.*) That's where I got you both wrong! (*To* SLIM.) You, boy, get yourself out to the kitchen and stir up some cakes that a man won't break his teeth on. (*To* OLE.) And you, don't you ever change your shirt or I'll forget you're a blacksmith again, for sure!

(*Both men go off happily in opposite directions.* PAUL *follows D.L. in the direction of the blacksmith's shanty and* JOE *returns to* PETE.)

JOE. Yes, sir. That's how it was. But they turned out to be the best men in camp for all that. And Paul didn't ever forget that the joke was on him.

PETE. (*Laughing.*) That's pretty good! But I mind how later on camp grew, and Slim couldn't bake enough cakes in a week to last through one meal. Well, that was why they built the big griddle. 'Course it was Paul's idea. And it worked fine—lasted for years. Paul figured one griddle with a lot of cooks was worth more'n one cook with a lot of griddles. So he took the iron from two hundred plows and had a griddle made of 'em. Measured two hundred and thirty-five feet across when it was finished!

BOY IN AUDIENCE. How did they get it in the cook's shanty?

PETE. (*To the* BOY.) They couldn't, of course. So Paul, he had 'em dig a hole outside for the fire to go under.

GIRL IN AUDIENCE. Who put it there? How could they carry it?

PETE. (*Reasonably.*) Why, nobody could handle it, all made up. But Paul got another idea. That griddle was made just about five miles from the camp—straight uphill. So he just lifted it up on its side and let it spin down by itself. Landed right smack over the fire! (*As he finishes this bit of his story, he walks toward C. He takes a piece of chalk from his pocket and draws a huge circle on the floor.*) We'll say this is it.

(PAUL *enters from L. and crosses over to the griddle where* PETE *is standing, now a part of the scene.*)

PAUL. (*Pleased.*) Well, what do you think of it? Ought to work fine, eh?

PETE. Sure is a big feller. How you going to keep it hot, though?

PAUL. Like this. (*Calling off stage to the cook.*) Slim! Oh, Slim! (SLIM *appears almost at once from U.R.*) You can get your fire tenders busy now.

SLIM. Right, sir. (*Calling.*) Hey, there!

(*As he calls, four or five loggers come in and poke imaginary brush around the edges of the circle. They light and tend the fire in pantomime through the rest of this scene.*)

PETE. That's slick! But, well—how you going to keep her greased?

PAUL. (*Proudly.*) Thought of that, too. Your greasers ready, Slim?

SLIM. I'll get 'em. Right away, sir.

(*As he goes off stage R.,* PAUL *goes on to explain.*)

PAUL. 'Course you couldn't expect one feller to reach clean across by himself. But a crew of men with bacon on their feet could skate around and get her greased in no time.

(At this moment eight or ten BOYS ON ROLLER SKATES *come in single file from U.R. They skate around and around the griddle in a circle, and when the job is done, skate back off in the direction from which they appeared.* PAUL *follows them with* SLIM, *and* PETE *goes down to* JOE *again.)*

PETE. And so from then on that's how we kept the old griddle greased and the fellers fed.

JOE. *(Extending his hand.)* Put it there, son! I see you've been around the camps. But did you ever hear what became of that griddle?

PETE. *(Unwilling to admit he hasn't heard this one.)* No. Don't reckon I ever did. Still had it the last I heard.

JOE. *(Pleased to be able to spin this one.)* Well, this was some years after. 'Course every time we moved camp we took it with us. It was the best piece of equipment we had. Usually let the blue ox haul it—only creature that could. But this last trip was to South America. Paul didn't go account of he had business on the coast. He put his man, Dick Loomis, in charge. Seems as if everything was all right till they started back home and some bad weather came up around the Horn.

PETE. And Paul, where was he then?

JOE. Seattle. Waiting for Dick to come in. But the fleet was way overdue and Paul, he was getting mighty anxious.

BOY IN AUDIENCE. What were they doing in South America?

JOE. Timber! Always timber! Wasn't any land cleared between these two oceans that Paul didn't have a hand in. But getting back to this time, Paul wasn't along or maybe things wouldn't have happened like they did. *(Again* JOE *goes toward C. as he continues his story.*

PAUL *appears and the two men meet at C.*) Well, I was
with Paul. (*They gaze out over the audience as if looking out to sea.*) Don't see anything, sir. Not a ship any-
where in sight.

PAUL. (*Worried.*) Time they got back a week ago. Bar-
ring bad weather. Maybe I should have gone with them
myself.

JOE. Didn't have much cargo coming back.

PAUL. But we haven't heard if they got there at all.

(*A very ragged sailor,* DICK LOOMIS, *approaches from
D.L.—off stage—and calls to them.*)

DICK. (*Off.*) Halloo! (*Pause.*) Halloo, there!

PAUL. Someone calling, Joe?

JOE. Over there, sir. (*Pointing L.*) It's a seaman, I think.

PAUL. A seaman? (*Bellows in recognition.*) Why, it's our
captain, Dick Loomis! What's happend to you, son?

(DICK *enters.*)

DICK. (*Staggering up to them.*) Bad weather, sir. Down
at the Horn. Got through all right going, but coming
back she let go. There isn't much left of the fleet.

JOE. How come you're alone?

DICK. Got kind of scattered, sir, when she went down.

PAUL. But how did you get back?

DICK. Made me a raft of the crowbars on my ship and
floated all the way home. Been living on sea biscuits for
weeks.

PAUL. And the crew?

DICK. We all did the same, sir. They'll likely come floating
in, too, one at a time.

PAUL. You better come inside and have some hotcakes right
now before you finish your story.

DICK. (*Desperately.*) One thing I've got to tell you, sir,
first! Speaking of hotcakes, the worst thing of all! The
big griddle was on the head ship—and when the winds

came up, off she rolled! Right off the deck into the water! And the last thing I saw of her, she was stuck there! Straight up—dividing the Atlantic from the Pacific, so help me!

(PAUL *puts a comforting arm around* DICK's *shoulder and they walk off together.* JOE *goes back to* PETE.)

JOE. Yes, sir, that's where she landed and that's where she sits.

BOY IN AUDIENCE. And what did Paul do for hotcakes after that?

JOE. Well, young feller, they say he got a new griddle in Minneapolis, even bigger. I wouldn't know for sure, 'cause I wasn't there. I left about then and came out here.

GIRL IN AUDIENCE. But what happened to Paul Bunyan? And his blue ox?

PETE. Some say he went back to New England——

JOE. And I heard he's up in Alaska, still felling trees. The ox died. But Paul, well it doesn't much matter. Those of us who knew him won't ever forget.

PETE. Hasn't been such logging in these parts since.

JOE. (*Consulting his watch or a clock.*) Well, time I was getting along. It sure flies when you talk. Nice to have met you, young feller. (*To the audience.*) And you folks, out there, if you want to hear more stories sometime, why, there's lots more to tell. But the way to hear the best yarns is to get two old loggers together.

(JOE *and* PETE *shake hands warmly and leave the stage,* JOE *to the L. and* PETE *to the R. The stories are over and the audience also goes home.*)

Production Notes

COSTUMES:

If costumes are to be used—and since we are not using scenery, it would seem a decided advantage to use them —all of the men should be dressed as lumberjacks. Denim and corduroy pants, wool shirts and boots, jackets, and even coonskin caps can be worn to obtain variety.

PAUL BUNYAN may be a child on stilts or a very tall boy padded to give the effect of one much larger than the others. Much or little effort may go into the making up of this figure but the more powerful he appears, the more extraordinary the character.

SLIM wears a clean blue shirt and trousers.

OLE wears a very dirty outfit by contrast.

DICK wears very ragged clothes, bare feet, and no hat.

PROPERTIES:
    table
    2 kitchen or simple wooden chairs
    plate of hotcakes
    roller skates for the griddle greasers

BIBLIOGRAPHY

Cassady, Marsh, *Playwriting Step by Step*. San Jose, CA: Resource Publications, 1992. Easy-to-follow book for young readers and adults on the basics of writing a play: originating ideas, dialogue, characters, standard plot structure, theatre styles. Explanations of theory, procedures and exercises. Available from Empire Publishing Service, P.O. Box 1344, Studio City, CA 91614.

____, *Storytelling Step by Step*. San Jose, CA: Resource Publications, 1990. An accessible guide to effective storytelling, using voice, props and gesture.

____, *Creating Stories for Storytelling*. San Jose, CA: Resource Publications, 1991. How to judge your audience and tailor your storytelling to them effectively and entertainingly.

Doolittle, Joyce, *ed.*, *Playhouse: Six Fantasy Plays for Children*. Toronto, Ontario: Northern Lights/Red Deer College Press, 1989. Internationally acclaimed children's theatre expert selects six exciting plays for young audiences ranging from kindergarten through junior high school. Available from Empire Publishing Service, P.O. Box 1344, Studio City, CA 91614.

James, JoAnne, *Three Quest Plays for Children*. Studio City, CA: Players Press, 1996. Three funny, poignant, clever and contemporary plays exploring the hazards and joys of friendship, by an award-winning children's dramatist.

Korty, Carol, *Writing Your Own Plays, 2nd Edition*. Studio City, CA: Players Press, 2000. A creative process for writing and developing plays for children.

Landes, William-Alan, *Wondrawhopper Plays*. Studio City, CA: Players Press, 1968-85.

Aladdin n'His Magic Lamp	*Rapunzel n'The Witch*
Alice n'Wonderland	*Peter n'The Wolf*
Indian Tales	*Robin Hood*
Jack n'The Beanstalk	*Rhyme Tyme*
The Wizard of Oz	*Rumpelstiltskin*

A series of highly producable plays that have been performed, toured and presented in classrooms and theatres around the world. Bright, entertaining and carefully crafted for children of all ages, Very flexible casts which can be easily expanded. *Rhyme Tyme* is one of the most popular plays and is easily produced.

Morton, Miriam, ed., *A Harvest of Russian Children's Literature*. Berkeley, CA: 1967. A comprehensive collection of prose and poetry originating in Russian and translated/adapted to English. A wealth of material for the classroom teacher and specialist.

Rosenberg, Joel, ed., ¡Applauso!: Hispanic Children's Theatre. Houston, TX: Arte Público Press, 1995. Award-winning bilingual theatre director brings together six pieces by six acclaimed Hispanic playwrights. English and Spanish language plays. Available from Empire Publishing Service, P.O. Box 1344, Studio City, CA 91614.

Sawyer, Ruth, ed., *The Way of the Storyteller*. Revised Edition. New York: Penguin Books, 1977. Various different ways of telling and choosing stories, stories to tell and a reading list.

Thistle, Louise, *Dramatizing the Little Red Hen / Dramatizando la Gallinita Roja*. San Diego CA: Literature Dramatization Press, 1995. Two stand-alone volumes (can also be purchased and used as a set) offering a clear, simple way to develop language and literature through drama. Ideal for beginning readers, bilingual education and Spanish-English transition instruction for younger students. Available from Empire Publishing Service, P.O. Box 1344, Studio City, CA 91614.

Trelease, Jim, *The Read-Aloud Handbook*. New York: Penguin Books, 1982. The author tells how reading aloud awakens the listener's imagination, improves language skills and opens doors to a new world of entertainment. An important inclusion is a list of 300 annotated fairy tales, short stories, poems and novels that the author describes in detail with suggested age and grade levels. Available from Empire Publishing Service, P.O. Box 1344, Studio City, CA 91614.

INDEX

Theatre Books from PLAYERS PRESS

SILLY SOUP   by Carol Korty
A excellent collection of humorous short plays and skits based on classic folktale traditions. Popular and entertaining. Bibliography. **128 pp   pb   6 X 9   0-88734-679-0**

PLAYS FROM AFRICAN FOLKTALES   by Carol Korty
Charming, entertaining adaptations of classic African folk tales for performance by younger performers, with musical, costuming and language tips. Bibliography, Discography.
112 pp   pb   6 X 9   0-88734-659-6

101 THEATRE GAMES   by Mila Johansen
A critically acclaimed workbook. This popular hands-on theatre game book covers Warm-Up Games, Storytelling, Mime, Exercises, and much more. Explicit enough for beginners but sophisticated enough for the advanced performer. **160 pp   pb   8.5 X 11   0-88734-911-0**

LOOK, LISTEN AND TRUST by Rawlins and Rich
Structural/material theatre games to enhance performance and social skills. Ideal for high school teachers and students.
192 pp   pb   6 X 9   0-88734-618-9

PLAYING THE GAME   by Christine Poulter
100 step-by-step theatre games that can be used to develop acting, social and personal skills.
160 pp   pb   5.5 X 8.5   0-88734-650-2

ASSIGNMENTS in Musical Theatre by Laughlin and Wheeler
Techniques for pre-performance analysis for musical theatre performers and directors. A great source for novice and professional, student and teacher. Illustrated.
192 pp   pb   8.5 X 11   0-88734-676-6

Available at your local bookstore or directly from:
Players Press P.O. Box 1132, Studio City CA 91614-0132

More Books from PLAYERS PRESS

THE CURTAIN RISES Volume I by Paula Gaj Sitarz
The history of theatre from its origins in Greece and Rome through the English Restoration. Visually attractive with numerous drawings, illustrations and photographs. Suited to introductory theatre classes from elementary schools through college.   **144 pp   pb   8.5 X 11 0-88734-685-5**

THE CURTAIN RISES Volume II   by Paula Gaj Sitarz
The history of theatre from 19th century England to the modern times. Visually oriented with numerous photos, illustrations and drawings. An ideal text for all grades.
          144 pp   pb   8.5 X 11 0-88734-678-2

THE CURTAIN RISES Volume III   by Paula Gaj Sitarz
The history of theatre from its roots in the Old World to its fruition in the New Worlds of Australia, Canada, South Africa and America. Lavishly illustrated, suited for introductory classes at all grade levels.
          144 pp   pb   8.5 X 11 0-88734-689-8

CREATIVE MOVEMENT for 3-5 year olds by Harriet H. Forbes
Fundamentals of movement and dance. 35 weekly lesson plans. Dance notations, illustrations, pronunciations, and definitions. Music and poetry for each lesson. A guide to enriching your curriculum, enrollment, and income.
          248 pp   pb   8.5 X 11   0-9659944-1-4

THE AMERICAN MUSICAL THEATRE   by Stephen Porter
An indispensable guide for student and professional — a history, production blueprint, critical guide, and source of projects and assignments. Ideal for student, writer and critic, actor or director, producer or teacher. Illustrated.
          128 pp   pb   8.5 X 11 0-88734-686-3

Available at your local bookstore or directly from:
Players Press P.O. Box 1132 Studio City CA 91614-0132